ISBN: 978-1-4507-6775-0

Published by: Hanson House

Hanson House is a division of:
Heads-Up Performance, Inc.
12852 Big Sur Drive • Tampa, FL 33625 • 813-968-8863

www.PlayBigTraining.com

Illustrations and Book Design by:
Todd Pearl

Back Cover photo: Eric Chase

A great baseball story with vital lessons for life.

Mental Toughness Secrets That Take Baseball Players To The Next Level

Dr. Tom Hanson

Illustrations and book design by Todd Pearl

Prologue

**Sometimes the game you think you're playing
isn't really the game you're playing.**

About The Author

Tom Hanson has dedicated his life to helping athletes and business leaders "*Play Big.*"

Dr. Tom Hanson

Mental game expert, executive coach and professional speaker, Hanson has brought his cutting edge approach to performance to baseball players from Little Leaguers to big league World Series Champions, including the New York Yankees, Texas Rangers and individual major league players. He consults with Fortune 500 companies, such as Microsoft, Verizon and Kaiser Permanente, and smaller businesses, transforming team and individual performance.

Hanson believes dramatic improvement is possible. Anyone can break through their current limits and play big – on the field or in life – if they're willing to challenge their current thinking and follow some simple steps.

Hanson has a Ph.D. in education specializing in sport psychology from the University of Virginia, where he also served as hitting coach. From 1991 to 1998 he taught sport psychology and was the head baseball coach at Skidmore College. He left his tenured position there to

found Heads-Up Performance, Inc., an international consulting and coaching company.

His first book, Heads-Up Baseball: Playing the Game One Pitch at a Time, co-authored with Dr. Ken Ravizza, has been called "the bible for learning mental toughness in baseball" and was required reading for the U.S. Olympic baseball team and many pro teams.

His second book, Who Will Do What By When: How to Improve Performance, Accountability and Trust with Integrity, co-authored with his wife and business partner Birgit Zacher Hanson, MCC, has empowered thousands of leaders with a step-by-step guide for manifesting their vision.

He is a world leader in the elimination of the "yips" in baseball players, golfers, and others.

Hanson lives with his wife Birgit and children CJ and Angelina in Tampa, Florida.

For More Information Visit:

PlayBigTraining.com – *Get free training based on this book*

YipsBeGone.com – *If you or someone you know is having trouble making easy throws, putts, or anything else, visit this site now.*

HeadsUpPerformance.com – *For business team and individual performance enhancement.*

Testimonials

The following are just some of the hundreds of people who believe in and have benefitted from the systems you will discover in *"PLAY BIG"*:

"Before I had half completed this book, I had my team together talking through the principles Dr Tom Hanson speaks about! What a unique and creative way to present us with necessary building blocks to be our very best. We all want to play big, but how many really know how to prepare ourselves to do so day in and day out? Play Big gives us that process in a way that will be enjoyable for players and coaches alike to read."

Scott Brosius
1998 World Series MVP
Head Coach, Linfield College
Manager, 2011 Team USA 18U

"If you dream of success on the highest level on or off the field I urge you to listen to this guy. He's helped me tremendously."

Jarrod Saltalamacchia
Boston Red Sox

"It is almost like cheating to get so much practical instruction in how to build a mindset for success from a novel about baseball, but that is what Dr. Tom Hanson offers you with PLAY BIG. Reading it is a totally enjoyable way to get free coaching from a sports psychologist who has helped star athletes perform at their best."

Donna Eden and **David Feinstein**, *Ph.D*
Co-Authors, *The Promise of Energy Psychology*

"PLAY BIG is not only an easy read but a necessary read if you want to attract what you want in your life. Many thanks to Dr. Tom Hanson for putting together a delightful, engaging story with essential wisdom for all of us whether we are on or off the field. While most of us could have used these principles and techniques decades ago, it's never too late to succeed! Use the gifts Tom is offering in PLAY BIG and enjoy the powerful shifts in your life."

Carol Look, LCSW, DCH, EFT Master
Author, *Attracting Abundance with EFT*
AttractingAbundance.com

"PLAY BIG is a brilliant introduction to the science of intentionality. Hanson cleverly and skillfully combines a wonderful story with otherwise complex theories and principles in a way that's enjoyable and simple to understand. It's a worthy successor to Millman's classic Way of the Peaceful Warrior."

Eric Leskowitz, MD *Harvard Medical School*
Author, *"The Joy of Sox: Weird Science and the Power of Intention"*
TheJoyOfSoxMovie.com

"What a brilliantly crafted book! In this entertaining masterpiece of a baseball novel Dr. Tom Hanson reveals a lifetime of mental game secrets many Big Leaguers don't even know. Have you ever had the nagging feeling that there was something bigger out there for you to know? In PLAY BIG you will discover what that something bigger is."

Dave Hilton,
Former Major League Player and Coach
First Overall Draft Pick, 1971
ArizonaSchoolofBaseball.com

"I'm not an athlete, but WOW!, *you don't have to be to love this book. This applies to everyone. The first time I tried the ABC's I knocked the socks off the teachers I was coaching and created a breakthrough turning point for them."*

Linda Cordes, Teacher Coach,
www.RedHotTeaching

PLAY BIG

"Tom has done an excellent job putting the principles of the Mental Game into literary format. His creative ability to discuss the mental skills of performance in an engaging manner is truly exceptional. He also presents new ideas on techniques for energy management. This book can definitely help someone improve their performance on and off the field."

Ken Ravizza, Ph.D.
Co-author, *"Heads-Up Baseball"*
American Baseball Coaches Association Hall of Fame

"If you were to ask the greatest ball players who ever lived how much of their sport is mental, the most common answer would be '90%.' With this in mind you'd think most instructional books would focus on the inner game, but sadly, very few mention it at all. In Dr. Tom Hanson's PLAY BIG, the inner game of baseball is covered in such great detail that your outer game will improve almost immediately. Want to hit homeruns and throw no-hitters in baseball – or the game of life itself, then PLAY BIG is your ticket to the stadium where the biggest games are always played out first."

Matt Furey, World Shuai-Chiao Kung Fu Champion, Author of fitness best-seller: *Combat Conditioning*, *MattFurey.com*

"*PLAY BIG is the perfect story for a lasting impact. I loved the way it engaged all the senses to impart results – not just through sports psychology but energy psychology as well. I couldn't put it down, and it's now required reading for all my clients!*"

Gina Parris, Performance Coach
BuiltToWinCoaching.com

"*Your book is amazing. My new Holy Grail. This is quite simply the best performance book I have read and I feel like I've read them all. It will transform the lives of any player open-minded enough – and lucky enough – to read it.*"

Sean Grey, Performance Success Coach
StageFrightFreedom.com

"*Dr. Tom Hanson is one of our nation's best and brightest teachers. I have worked with Tom for more than four years and I know first-hand that any parent or coach who wants to be sure that their young athletes are developing age-appropriate mental and emotional skills through sport would be well-served by learning from Tom.*"

Mark Siwik, Executive Director, *BeLikeCoach*
BeLikeCoach.com

"I only bring in the best to speak at my Ultimate Pitching Coach camps and Dr. Tom Hanson is a regular. He's a master teacher and storyteller. I strongly encourage any young person, parent or coach to utilize Tom's work to inspire, educate and motivate."

Ron Wolforth, *TexasBaseballRanch.com*

*"Dr. Tom's first book, **Heads-Up Baseball**, changed my life and the lives of the players I worked with for over 15 years. You should see my copy of it - so worn, dog eared and highlighted it's barely hanging together. But, I will NEVER give it up. It's one of the prized possessions of my baseball library. So let me give you a "heads up:" PLAY BIG will change your life. It is a mandatory reading for any coach, player or parent who wants to be successful in the game of baseball. I would stand behind anything Dr. Tom Hanson does. He is one of the great people in baseball!"*

Paul Reddick, *"The Master of MPH"*
90mphClub.com

"If 90% of this game is half mental, then everyone should call Dr.Tom. I recommend him to players of any age regardless of level, as he helps everyone who gets near him."

Billy Martin, Jr., Player Agent

"Dr. Tom Hanson has done it again. First, in the mid-1990s to boost sports performance, he was a leader in bringing cognitive psychology methods to baseball as a co-author of the baseball classic, **Heads-Up Baseball***. Now, he is leading the way as a pioneering sports-performance expert boldly bringing innovative, effective and dependable body-energy based methods into the mainstream of the baseball world through a creative baseball novel. I used the tapping methods described in this book with the* **Oregon State University** *baseball team that won back-to-back College World Series championships in 2006 & 2007 – let me tell you: they work!"*

Greg Warburton, MS, LPC
Sports Performance Consultant
GregWarburton.com

"In 2004 I was killed in a car wreck. I obviously didn't stay dead but I saw some amazing things during that time and I can tell you, Dr. Tom, you are exactly right, what you wrote in PLAY BIG. See, I saw it first hand. Its all energy and all about what you choose to send out, positive or negative. I tell people this but I think they go along with it till I am gone and then they laugh at what a kook I must be. Well, when I read this book it hits it right on the head! You are exactly right!"

Kevin Kenneally, Assistant Baseball Coach
Lebanon High School, Ohio

"I love stories. I especially love stories that teach. And this one does – BIG time. Dr. Hanson has woven vast quantities of profound knowledge into a truly inspiring tale. If you want more confidence, greater achievement and also have more fun, PLAY BIG is a must-read."

Michael Angier, CEO
www.SuccessNet.org

"Dr. Tom Hanson has dedicated his life to discovering the best methods for playing big – for not only playing one's best, but also enjoying the game more fully and developing one's full potential. This book outlines in a brilliant way the culmination of this journey. Read this book. It provides practical insights, tools and exercises that will help you on and off the field."

Sean Brawley, Performance Coach
SeanBrawley.com

"Tom's advice and guadance has catapaulted a number of our clients to much higher performance levels. He is the best!!"

Dr. Jim Vigue, Super Health Nation
Former USA Baseball Major League PlayerEsAssociation Coach of the Year, Editor of Peak Power Baseball

Acknowledgements

Thank you to my wonderful wife, Birgit, not only are you a Master Certified Coach, but more importantly a masterful partner and mother; and to my kids Christopher (CJ) and Angelina for your loving energy – focusing on you puts me in "The Bigs" every time; and to my Mom and Dad for your unwavering lifetime of support.

Thank you to Todd Pearl (*ToddPearl.com*) for your creative genius in the illustrations and overall look and feel of the book; to Linda Cordes (RedHotTeaching.com) for your cheer-leading and generous, sharp-witted edits; and Matt Fulks (MattFulks.com) for skillfully tightening the manuscript. Special thanks to Jim Vigue for course correcting the book; and Ivy Gilbert for vital layout coaching; and media legend Eric Chase for your photo work; and to Erika Herrmann, Jim Hanson, Petra Boehm, and George Hanson (you guys are like family to me). To Moorhead (MN) High School English teachers Ken Tangen and Bud Melting, you taught me to write and my gratitude continues.

I've drawn from too many teachers throughout my career to thank them all here. I must, though, thank Esther and Jerry Hicks and their friends Abraham (Abraham-Hicks.com). Anyone familiar with their work will recognize it throughout this book, especially the vertical continuum of feelings

and the teachings around the Law of Attraction. Thank you to Ken Ravizza for decades of mentoring and friendship. The "Performance = Potential – Interference" model is taken directly from Timothy Gallwey's great Inner Game of Tennis teachings.

Thank you to energy psychology coaches Donna Eden, Carol Look, Steve Wells, Patricia Carrington, Jimmy Mack (and friends), and Gary Craig (founder of EFT and well-being philanthropist); Thank you to good friends Sean Brawley, Peter Illig and Billy Strean for being true friends, to "Tapper Bob" Gilpatrick and Kathy Perry who got me tapping, and to tapping buddies Gina Paris, Dave Hilton, and Sean Grey, and Angye Fox and Andrea Masciana for many things.

Thank you to baseball training gurus Matt Furey and Paul Reddick for your coaching, and Glenn Dietzel for yours. To my Moorhead American Legion Blues (1980-81) and Luther College Norse (1981-1985) baseball teammates and coaches – several of whom appear fictitiously in this book – my fond memories of the laughs and wins are non-fiction. And my deepest gratitude to the hundreds of players, coaches, executives and others I've had the privilege to learn from and coach.

TABLE OF CONTENTS

Do not READ this book

… Instead, I challenge you to FEEL your way through it.

I wrote this book as a story to help the energy it contains sneak past your thinking brain and embed itself where it needs to be for you to breakthrough to the next level: in your body.

As you read, notice how you feel. Do the exercises along with "21" and see what you discover about your thoughts and feelings.

People always say baseball is a "mental game." True, but I say it's an "emotional game." Think about it: do you say "I'm thinking confident," or do you say "I feel confident?"

Do you say "I'm thinking negative thoughts about my game lately," or do you say "I feel horrible at the plate?"

Emotions rule the day. You perform consistent with how you feel. When you feel great, you:

1. Play better

2. Enjoy it more

The essential question that separates the greats from the failures is: "Are you in charge of your feelings, or are your feelings in charge of you?"

Despite saying "confidence is 90% of success," a typical pitcher will spend 100x more time developing his changeup

than developing his ability to "change up" his confidence when he fails. That's just wrong.

This book puts the power to make your dreams come true literally at your finger tips. It puts your hands directly on the controls in a way you've never even imagined.

Will you feel 100% unstoppable all the time and win every game if you master the contents of this book? No. Life doesn't work that way.

But the book will enable you to avoid massive pain. Not just the pain of one failure on the field, but the pain that comes from knowing you fell short of your potential. The pain that rips through your gut from knowing you robbed yourself of the fun of performing at your peak. The pain that I had after my career.

Brace Yourself for the Second Half!

The first half of the book is rock solid. Every right-minded player, coach and parent can understand the benefit of the ABC's. They've helped so many players for so many years – I know they will work for you.

But get ready. In the second half, I challenge you to stretch yourself in a new and exciting direction. I reveal what is REALLY happening on the field and what you need to do to take control. Be prepared. You may be shocked. You may want to argue. You may even laugh. Go ahead.

But remember your reaction ten years from now when the contents of this book are as routine as strength and condi-

tioning training is today. (Are you old enough to remember when strength training was considered "bad"? How about all the people who thought the earth was flat?)

The question is: Are you going to buy in now and have the edge, or wait ten years until everyone else is doing it—and your career is over?

Devour every page of this book and you will have a huge advantage over those unlucky enough to have not found this book or who are too close-minded to try it.

Is that an arrogant statement? You decide. I'm just talking with the conviction you too would have if, like me, you'd seen this information help thousands of people transform their game and their lives.

Finally, the key to success in baseball and the rest of life is training. Practice. But what should you practice? How should you practice it? Those are the million dollar questions.

The answers lie in the pages ahead.

Remember, don't read, feel.

Success is something you feel your way to.

Part 1:

Do You Make These Mistakes Hitting and Pitching?

You're about to discover...

- **How NOT to Hit (and pitch)**

- **The most important question in baseball**

- **Why you must fail to have fun**

- **The hidden cause of technical mistakes**

- **The *REAL* source of your results**

How Not to Hit

The streaking fastball was belt high,
right down Main Street central.

My eyes lit up as my front foot stomped into the ground. "I'll rip this pitch," I said to myself as I yanked my hands forward.

And I *needed* to rip it.

The last couple of weeks were a nightmare for me at the plate: two for my last 23 and both those hits were lame. One hit was a swinging bunt that actually stopped on the foul line — my only whiff of good luck in this whole streak. I'd already struck out and popped up today.

I'd moped around complaining about my slump to anyone who'd listen and I was wound up tight for this game.

But the team needed me to come through. This was the fourth inning of Game 2 of the best-of-three Red River Valley Summer League Championship.

We'd won Game 1 by a run (with no help from me) and we wanted this championship bad. After a slow start to the season our team had really come together and run the table the last few weeks, winning the first two rounds of the postseason tournament 9-1 and 8-2, and winning Game 1 of the championship series 3-2.

We had a special group of players who now shared a special bond, and although it was just a summer league, we wanted the laughs and life-long memory of dog piling at the end of the season.

But it wouldn't come easily.

The Rakeops, in their signature black tops and crazed dog logo black and white hats, had jumped out to a 3-1 lead in this second game, and our bats had gone silent.

Winning this game was huge because the Rakeops had their ace, Jay Kamin (Ka-MEAN), ready to pitch tomorrow's possible Game 3. Kamin was the Red River Valley League's own Cy Young. He was nasty and had dominated all summer. In fact, he was unbeaten. He shut us out the only time we faced him this summer and his ERA of 1.98 was only that high because he'd been shaky in the first inning several times.

"Get him early or forget it," was the book on Kamin, and as yet no one had gotten him. Fortunately for us he pitched the game to get the Rakeops into the championship series so he wasn't available for these first two games.

So while we were in the driver's seat having won Game 1, the pressure was on to put them away here before they could get to Kamin.

And I was our best chance. The way I was hitting it was a fat chance, but a chance nonetheless.

We had runners on second and third, but there were two outs and I was in the hole with two strikes. The way we were having trouble scoring runs, we knew this could be the ballgame even though it was only the fourth inning (each of the best-of-three series games were seven innings).

I had been pretty nervous all day, and got even more so before this at-bat. When I got to the on-deck circle my heart

was pounding high in my chest, the butterflies were churning in my stomach, my hands felt clammy, and everything seemed to be going faster and faster. If you've been overly nervous about anything, you know the feeling.

I was so amped up, the start of our (bottom) half of the first inning was a blur.

Doug Kovash, the Rakeops' second-best pitcher, had been strong for three innings but walked the first batter in the fourth. Our two-hole hitter, Joe Knight, popped up. Jim George singled, putting runners on first and second, and both runners moved up one base when our clean-up guy and team slow poke, Kevin Dotseth, dribbled a nubber to first.

Suddenly the fate of the game, and perhaps the series, fell on my shoulders.

A baseball-sized lump in my throat choked my breath as I gingerly raked the dirt in the batter's box with my spikes.

I had decided to take the first pitch to see if Kovash was still in control and to run up his pitch count. Of course, it was a fastball down the middle for strike one.

Fortunately, Kovash followed with two pitches well out of the strike zone so they were easy takes. Perhaps his control was wavering.

"Time to shine," I thought to myself, *"he'll come with one now."*

The 2-1 offering was a fastball alright. I grunted my swing through the zone and fouled it back.

Two balls and two strikes.

"Big one left," I thought as I stepped out of the box, "rip it and be the hero... "OR STRIKE OUT AND BE THE GOAT!" came another, more powerful voice in my head.

I squeezed the bat tightly and locked down my jaw as I stepped into the box. "Don't strike out," the voice said, fearing the worst and praying Kovash would throw that first fastball again.

"THERE IT IS!" said my inner alarms the instant the ball left the Kovash's right hand, "JUST LIKE THE FIRST PITCH!"

This fastball was in my happy zone... This fastball was crushable... This fastball was....

... a curveball.

The instant I actually saw the ball, the dang thing was tumbling like clothes in a dryer, and it was obvious the pitch would be way outside.

But it was too late.

As a psychology major I'd always been fascinated with things like that moment in time when you've committed to some action, be it slamming the car door or swinging at a pitch, and you realize you've made a mistake.

It seems like you should have plenty of time to stop, but the horse has left the barn. You just can't stop.

This time, *fascinating* isn't the word I would use to describe the experience.

My butt shot out behind me like I was begging to be spanked and I hideously lurched forward in hopes of fouling it off. But I already told you how my luck was running. My streak remained alive and well.

I got my spanking alright: strike three.

Embarrassingly, the only thing that did hit the ball was the dirt in the lefty batter's box. In disgust I continued my futile flail at the ball by spinning my body around like a top, looking up to the sky in submission.

I'd twirled myself right onto home plate when the catcher tagged me out. Add "not-running-to-first-base-on-strike-three-in-the-dirt" to my distinguished list of accomplishments for the at-bat.

I took my helmet off with my right hand and smacked it into the palm of my left hand as the Rakeops hustled off the field to the cheering of their 60 or so fans. I could feel the deflation in my teammates as they tried their best to jog out of our first base dugout to take the field for the fifth inning.

"Here we go again," I said to myself. *"I stink!"*

I'd let the team down again. Tough to win tournaments when your number-five hitter can't put the ball in play, much less drive in a run.

As I walked toward my defensive position at first base, Johnny Waddle, our catcher, gave me my hat and glove. He gave me a quick word of encouragement, but I didn't catch what it was.

I was lost in my own world of loser-dom.

I continued my self-lynching as I got to first and began angrily chucking ground balls to the infielders.

"DANG IT!" I blurted out through my gritted teeth.

Then, *"Atta boy, Tom,"* I said to myself sarcastically as I flung a ball to third. *"Way to come through for the team."*

**While I knew I stunk as a player,
what I didn't know was that this dark night of my soul
was actually the dawning of the most important,
most shocking, and most wonderful
experience of my life so far.**

**In fact, I was just a few outs from the start of an
adventure that may, before this is all over,
change the way baseball is played forever.**

Although this was just the top of the fifth and we still had nine outs left (we always play 7 inning games in this league), I felt like it was all over. Not just the game and not just the series, but my whole baseball career. *Why play if I can't hit?*

Baseball Doesn't Care

After we got the Rakeops out damage-free in the top of the fifth (during which I continued verbally abusing myself), I

trotted in to the dugout. Having made the last out of the fourth (shocker) I had some time on my hands.

I was too intent on beating myself up to appreciate how nice a day it was.

August in northwest Minnesota, the tail end of "Road Construction Season" as we refer to summer up here, can really be beautiful. Today was just that: 76 degrees and sunny with those fluffy, Chamber of Commerce "come visit our 10,000 lakes" clouds overhead.

No chance of rain. But even in the radiance of this fine day, somehow Old Man Winter was sending advance notice we shouldn't get too comfortable, he'd be back soon.

I, like all Minnesota males, considered myself above average. Tall with limited speed and mobility (that's what I was told, although in my mind I was cat-like quick), I was confined to playing first base. Three right arm operations stemming from a childhood accident made my throwing a team joke.

But there was nothing wrong with my glove hand – I could pick it with anybody.

Until recently I was also a good hitter. From youth league through junior high I was consistently a dominating hitter (it helped to be a head taller than most), but it seemed other guys caught up to me in my early teens.

I wrongfully sat the bench during my junior year: *How could you not find a place for a guy who was ripping the ball like I was?*

But riding the bench actually worked out pretty well in the long run because it motivated me to practice hard the winter of my senior year. I swung a weighted bat in the basement (still sorry about the chunk I took out of the pool table, Dad) and read Charlie Lau's book on hitting for hours. I even flipped through the corner pages, setting in motion George Brett's swing, until the pages were so frayed that the images wouldn't come to life anymore. But, man, I wanted to hit like Brett. Who didn't!

Everything came together the summer of my senior year of American Legion ball. I even set some records that had stood for awhile.

But unfortunately for me baseball doesn't care what you've done in the past.

It doesn't care what you're capable of.

It just gives you what you've got coming on this next pitch.

Like the Greek character Sisyphus rolling his rock up the hill only to have it roll back down again, each time up to the plate you start over from scratch.

And right now, for today's game, I felt I should be scratched from the lineup.

As I entered the newly painted light blue first-base dugout, my metal cleats click-clacked on the cement steps. I grabbed a paper cup, filled it with water from the yellow cooler, and gulped it down while my teammates milled around.

"Let's get this guy," said one of my teammates trying to overcome the unspoken sense that we might not pull this one out and our joyous one game lead could turn into a crushing series defeat if we had to beat Kamin (we'd yet to ever score off him).

I grunted some faux support and stepped just outside the dugout to the outfield side to blow off some steam.

Matson Field had improved dramatically in just the past year. The old four-foot fence was replaced with a 7-foot high chain link fence that began on the outfield end of our first-base dugout and encircled the entire outfield, both foul and fair territory.

A new grounds guy had the field in nice shape and they'd dramatically improved the lights. A light green windscreen ran the whole length of the fence, which gave the field that cool, Big League enclosed feeling.

Nowhere is that more important than in Moorhead, Minnesota, *God's pool table.*

This area is astonishingly flat. If you ever wonder how far you can see on a flat surface, come to Moorhead.

And it's crazy windy. Today was pretty calm, but generally it felt like the wind raced down the east side of the Rocky Mountains, accelerated as it crossed Montana and North Dakota, and slammed into every human face in Moorhead. Not a pleasant feeling, even in the summer. (You don't want to know about the winters).

So adding the windscreen was a major upgrade for the ballpark.

The windscreen had the unintended effect of making it hard for the players to see the fans through the screen.

With your face near the wind screen, you could see through the windscreen well enough, but put even a few inches between you and the fence and everything behind it blurred out fast. Fans milling about behind the fence were shadowy ghosts whose form you could make out, but you couldn't see the finer details that make a person recognizable.

All of that was fine with me at the moment. I didn't want to see anyone pointing at me as the loser who blew this for our team.

"Hey 21," a man's voice barked out my number through the screen. I didn't recognize the voice and was in no mood to chat or put up with him asking for a ball or something, so I ignored it.

"Hey 21, got a minute?" the voice persisted.

I turned to look at him. I couldn't tell much through the screen except that he was an adult (meaning older than me, so at least in his late 20s) a few inches over six feet tall. He was not fat, not skinny. I couldn't make out any facial features, but while he seemed familiar in some way, I was confident I didn't know the guy.

Turned out he knew me even better than I knew myself.

You're Asking for It

"How's it goin'?" he asked in a pretty non-descript accent. It wasn't the strong local "Minnesooda" accent, his vowel sounds weren't round enough. But it wasn't a strong Northeastern or Southern accent either, so perhaps a transplanted Minnesotan from Florida or something.

My icy stare back at the shadow in the fence made any verbal response to his question unnecessary.

"I see," he said before adding with some sarcasm,

"And how's that working for you?"

"How's what working for me?" I snapped back.

"It doesn't take supernatural powers to see you're pretty down on yourself," the man said, almost implying he had such powers. "This is a big game. I'd think you'd want to play big."

I took offense: "With all due respect, sir, I want more than anything to help this team. Did you see my last AB?" [AB = at bat, a hitter's turn at the plate]

"Yes," he said, "and?"

"And that's how it's going," I said with a tone and body language that made it clear I was done talking with him.

"Is that what you want to have happen?" he asked. "Is that how you want your game to go?"

"Yeah, sure, I love being the goat!" I said angrily. "Of course not! What do you think?" I then started heading back toward the dugout. I'd had enough of this harassment already.

"But you're playing small and asking for more of it," he said, "so I thought…"

"Look, I don't need some stranger coming over here and tell me I'm playing small, whatever that means. And I don't hear me asking for more crappy hitting, do you?"

"Actually, that's exactly what I'm hearing," laughed the man. "I can help you change that if you let me. *After all, you're actually only forgetting one thing.*"

"No thanks," I said only half turning back toward him as I kept walking. "I'm fine."

I stepped inside the dugout and stopped at the bench to grab some sunflower seeds from an open bag. I poured a handful, popped them all into my mouth, and headed for the home plate side of our dugout.

My mind was so busy being mad at myself and the stupid man that I didn't notice I was chewing the seeds whole. It didn't matter. It's not as if I had the patience to split each seed anyway.

"I'm asking for it?" I mumbled to myself, *"I'm playing small? And I'm forgetting 'only' one thing. Who does he think he is?"*

Ping!

I was snapped out of my own head by the familiar sound

of a baseball hitting a metal bat very hard. Kevin Dotseth, our center fielder, had just connected with a 2-1 pitch from Kovash. "Go ball! Go ball!" came the cries from our dugout as we all raced over the top step of the dugout.

"Yeaaahhhh!" we all cheered as Dotseth's ball barely cleared the right-field fence. "Dots" didn't have much opposite field power normally, but with Kovash's fastball providing the juice, he had just enough power to help us cut the lead to one run.

Is This Guy Serious?

While we were pumped up, Dotseth's home run didn't exactly rattle Kovash. He proceeded to mow down our next batters, and we were quickly back on the field.

Although I tried not to let the man see me look over, I glanced over at the man behind the screen several times from my position at first base.

Who is that guy? What does he want?
Is he pulling for the Rakeops and trying to get in my head to mess me up?

That doesn't make much sense, I'm already messed up.
He should ride someone on our team who might actually do something useful.

"This is a big game and
I thought you'd want to play big."

What kind of crap is that?
How could he think I'm asking for more bad hitting?

I'm only forgetting one thing?

What could that be? What am I forgetting?

All these questions made me want to punch him in the face. But I also wanted to find out the answers. He was in my head. I wish I knew who he was. He seemed so familiar, but not like anyone I'd met. He'd said he wanted to help, but so far he'd just helped me get more frustrated.

A strike out and two fly outs made short order of the Rake-ops' half of the fifth inning and I trotted in, head down.

I decided to forget the man and stay in the dugout where I belong.

The Most Important Baseball Question

"Same seats, same seats!" Chad Swanson, our shortstop, told everyone as we got into the dugout. He was the funny guy on the team (every team seems to have one), and he always seemed to be fired up about something.

He was invoking one of our rituals we'd created over the summer. The good teams I'd been on always made up their own goofy rally cries or superstitions (although they usually were both).

This one, "same seats," means we all go back to where we were during the previous inning. Since we'd scored while in those places, we all got back into them to start the bottom of the sixth.

PLAY BIG

"Wow," I thought to myself as it hit me: *I was outside talking to the man when the last inning started.* I couldn't believe I had to go back out there. It seemed a very strange coincidence that my decision to go out there a second time was made for me.

"Hey, 21," said the voice behind the screen in a welcoming tone as I took my position outside the dugout, "looks like the energy's changed and you guys have some momentum."

I grunted a reply.

"I didn't mean to get under your skin," the man said. "You just didn't look very happy and **I know you didn't know what you didn't know about playing this game.**"

For some reason, the way he said that melted just enough of the ice in my veins to crack me open.

"Okay," I said, "I'll bite. What one thing am I forgetting?"

"I'll answer with a simple question," he began. **"Why do you play baseball?"**

What? Come on, I thought, what kind of a question is that?

"Why do I play baseball?" I said. "Is that the best you've got?"

"Actually, yes, it is. It's the most important question in the game."

I nearly walked away again. I'd spent a whole inning trying to figure out what I was forgetting and the guy comes back with this "why do you play baseball?" garbage!

21

"Right now I have no idea," I said. "I don't even know why they let me play."

"Come down from the cross, man," he said sarcastically, "we need the wood. Tell me why you play and if you want I'll take off and leave you alone."

That sounded good. Here I was in a championship series game and I'm having a conversation with a man I don't know and can't even really see.

Just then Gary Thielen grounded out to short for the first out. That ended the "same seats" requirement and I now was free to go back inside the dugout. All I had to do was answer the man's question and I could get rid of him.

"I love it," I said angrily, "that's why I play."

"I see," said the man "and you're loving it now, right?"

I paused and took a breath. It was a smart aleck comment, but it stung. I was angry, but busted at the same time.

"No, of course I don't love this right now," I said, feeling beaten. "But, as they say, it is what it is."

"Okay," said the man, "never mind. That's a fair answer and I'll honor my commitment to leave any time you say. But you certainly haven't yet remembered what you forgot. I know it would help you if you did."

Part of me just wanted to get back to the dugout, hang with my teammates, and get ready to hit. But this guy was in

my dome. I just couldn't figure out how he could be familiar, know so much about me, and actually seem like a good guy ... but also be so annoying.

I was a desperate man and wanted to hear what he had to say.

"I'll bite again," I said, "what's the one thing I've forgotten?"

"I said you've forgotten this," he said, "but it's fairer to say you never really realized why you play."

"Sounds like you think you know why I play," I said, attitude back in full force.

"I'm certain I do," he said, raising the ante of the tone of the exchange.

"Fine. Lay it on me," I said.

Why You Play the Game

Even though this was a championship series, it still was a summer league game and we didn't have rules or pressures that we'd have in a school season, so it was okay for me to stand outside the dugout. I just had no idea how much hanging out I was about to do with this guy.

"I agree that you play baseball because you love it," he began, "you just aren't clear on what you love about it. On one level you love the way playing the game feels: the rush of the ball coming off the bat, the joy of letting go of a strong

throw, the connection with your teammates, the buzz of winning a game."

"Um, okay," I said.

"But there's no fun without failure."

"I bed your pardon?"

"Without failure," he added, "you wouldn't have fun playing baseball."

"Dude, you're crazy. You think I like failing?"

"No. But you wouldn't have any fun playing if you never failed."

I stared at the shadowy outline, tinkering with the idea. Is he serious?

"People always say baseball is a game of failure," the man continued. "And, sure, even a great big league hitter fails about seven out of ten at-bats. But baseball isn't a game of failure; it's a game of contrast."

"Contrast," I mumbled.

"Yes, you fail a lot, but then you succeed. That's contrast. You wouldn't play the game if you didn't experience contrast. The foundation of all games is people intentionally putting obstacles in their own way – be it the need to put a ball in a hole, whack it over a net or hit it with a bat, all the time keeping everything between the lines."

I nodded.

**"Why do we do that?" he rolled on
"because overcoming obstacles is fun. To overcome an obstacle you must focus and direct your energy on your target, on what you want. You have to grab your brain's reins and steer it to where you want it to go.**

"You have to gather all your energy and commit yourself fully. That's when you feel most alive, when you're summoning and focusing your energy. That's when you're what I call Big You. It feels good, it's enjoyable. It brings meaning to your life. If you succeeded all the time you wouldn't have to focus your energy. And that's boring."

I heard someone in our dugout shout encouragement to Kent Finanger, our right fielder who was trying to start a rally against Kovash. That woke me up enough to focus on the game for a second, even though my mind was still trying to wrap its arms around what the man was saying. I was still mad, but cooling.

"In addition to enjoyment," the man continued, "the obstacles force you to expand, to become more, bigger. Whether it's hitting a particular pitcher, getting a starting spot, moving up to the next level, whatever challenge the game is throwing at you right now, you have to expand, you're energy has to get bigger in order to overcome it. Just like your muscles come back bigger and stronger after you challenge them in the weight room, the rest of you has to expand to overcome the challenges you face on the field – and in the rest of your life for that matter."

I was starting to get caught up in his momentum.

"We all *crave* growth," he said. "We're born to expand. That's what life is about – a good life, anyway.

Those are the two things we want most in life: Enjoyment and Expansion. The two Es. I say what we all want is a life of Es.

We both paused for a moment and watched Kovash throw another nasty curve.

"So no," said the man, "you don't love the failure itself, but deep down you love the contrast. You enjoy the process of trying to overcome the challenges, and that very process causes you to expand. I like to say that outs give hits their meaning."

"You're getting pretty deep on me here, man."

"Okay," said the man, chuckling and shifting into a lighter gear. "Answer me this: if you got a hit every time how long do you think you'd play?

"Longer than you think, but okay, I get your point."

"Right. And if you got out every time..."

"I'd quit for sure," I said, visualizing myself doing just that.

"When you fail you experience what you don't want. But at the same time that experience reveals what you do want.

You, 21, just make the mistake of focusing on what you don't want instead of focusing on what you do want."

Again, I paused, processing.

Finanger was giving Kovash a battle, fouling off another pitch.

"Answer me this," said the man. "What do you not want today?"

"What do I *not* want? I don't want to suck. I don't want to choke. I don't want to let the team down by being an automatic out."

"And you don't want to feel…"

"Like I feel right now!" I said, my voice rising. "I don't want to feel like a loser. I don't want to be mad. I don't want to be afraid to hit."

"Great!" said the man.

Great? His enthusiasm for my suffering made me turn my head toward him. I wanted to see my tormentor.

"Now," he said, "use that clarity and energy to sling shot into telling me what you do want."

"I want to not feel like crap."

"No, no, no. What do you want? Listen to the question …

He paused as Kovash finally got Finanger to bounce a grounder to short. One out.

"What do you want?" the man asked again.

"Well," I said, struggling to change my mind from the 24-hour negativity channel playing inside, "I want to crush the ball again. I want to have fun. I want to help this team win."

"And you want to feel…"

"Confident. Like I know I can hit."

"Okay," the man said, in a way-to-go tone. "That's better. Do you feel the difference between what you don't want and what you do want? Do you get how big that gap is? The crappy feeling you have right now is simply your body telling you there's a huge gap between what you're focused on and what you want. Actually, it's between who you're acting like and who you really are. Baseball is harassing you into growth, 21. You have to expand to overcome the challenge you face right now. You need to Play Big. Isn't it exciting?"

"That's not the word I would use, but I think I get what you're saying."

He paused as Kovash got yet another ground ball out to short, two outs.

"Right now, at this moment, the game is calling you to adventure. It's calling you out. Will you answer the call and step up, or will you retreat back into your shell and suffer?"

I took a breath. I was still angry and down. But I did feel a pull inside me. A pull forward; a seed of possibility.

*Most players let
their thoughts
run wild.
To Play Big you
must first grab your
"brain's reins"
and begin
to control
your focus.*

I could tell the man was smiling as he said: "The game is calling you to answer baseball's most famous question."

"What's that?"

"Who's on first?"

That was clever, so clever I almost smiled.

We paused to soak in that major-league question as Joe Knight found himself down in the count, one ball and two strikes, to Kovash.

"But how do I do it?" I whined. "How do I go from this... this... this despair I'm feeling to feeling confident?"

"Fortunately, when heroes say yes to the call of adventure, help shows up out of nowhere. When the student is ready, the teacher appears. You just might not be able to see him."

"So you'll help me?"

"Yes. But only if you say yes to the call. It won't be easy, and we'll have to hurry. But along the way you'll find out a bunch more about just who is on first."

"Okay," I said, "I'm in."

Just then Knight grounded out sharply to third. Three outs. I grabbed my glove and headed out to first base.

The Hidden Cause
of Mechanical Mistakes

Bob Struebe, our hard-throwing lefty, had some control problems in the next inning. Sometimes the wheels just come off pitchers. I guess baseball was asking Struebe to expand. What he needed was the ump to expand the strike zone for him.

Before the blood bath was over, the Rakeops scored five runs, putting us behind, 8-2.

I didn't have long to talk to the man before I needed to get ready to hit, so I hustled and got to him well before the first pitch of the inning.

Although I wanted to get on with his "Play Big" training, I blurted out what was on the top of my mind: "Do I know you?"

"Not exactly," he said. "But we don't have time for that right now, you'll be up soon. What do you think is going on with your hitting?"

"I just keep pulling my front side open too early. I need to keep my shoulder closed."

"I saw that," said the man. "You even stepped in the bucket a bit and pulled your head off the ball."

I felt myself relax slightly. This mysterious stranger behind the screen might turn out to be a mass murderer, but at least he seemed to be paying attention and knew a little bit about the game.

He continued, "Do you really think it would help you to go up there next time and tell yourself: 'keep my shoulder closed, step right at the pitcher and keep my head down?'"

"Well," I said, knowing that was a lot to put in my head when hitting, "that's what I need to do."

"Why do you suppose you're opening up on your swing like that?" he asked, changing his angle of attack.

"If I knew that I wouldn't do it," I replied, with the beginning of an impatient edge. I thought he was going to help me, not play 20 questions.

"Did you do it two weeks ago before your slump started?"

Now the guy was starting to freak me out. This slump did start two weeks ago. *How did he know so much about me?*

"No," I said. "My swing was solid, efficient, mechanically sound. But pulling my front side open early and pulling my head is what started this whole slump, I think."

"But since you were hitting well before that, why would you start pulling your front side open?"

"I don't know," I said.

"Well, what controls your body?" the man asked.

"My brain, I guess. At least it should."

"And what does your brain do?"

"It thinks."

"So would it make sense to you if I said you most likely started pulling your front side open, which started your slump, *because you started thinking differently?* You probably either were trying to hit the ball out of the park or you were afraid of getting beat inside by a fastball."

That felt like it made sense, but he didn't give me time to think about it.

The man continued, "I like to deal with the source of problems, not symptoms. If you walk into a bathroom and the faucet is running and the sink is overflowing onto the floor, do you first go for a mop or turn off the faucet?"

"Turn off the faucet," I said.

"Exactly. Your thinking is the source of your problem. Pulling your front side open is just a symptom. **Your thoughts are the source of your results.** Let's see what happens when we work with the source."

The Source of Your Results

"So," the man started, "what have you been thinking about since your first AB?"

"Well," I said, still with attitude, but a bit more respectful than the inning before, "I'm like 2 for my last 200 and just struck out with a chance to drive in two runs in our biggest game of the season so far. So, big surprise here: I've been thinking about that."

"And how does that make you feel?" asked the man.

"Horrible! It sucks. I suck. I feel mad and frustrated. You'd feel horrible too if you were hitting like me."

"What I notice in what you're saying," said the man, completely unaffected by my pain, "is that there's a match between what you're thinking about and what you're feeling. You're thinking about how bad you're hitting and you're feeling bad. Is that correct?"

"Yes."

"Do you hit better when you're feeling good and feeling confident, or when you're feeling mad and frustrated?"

The answer was so obvious I stared toward his shadow to see if he was serious about wanting an answer. He didn't say anything. He was serious.

"When I'm feeling confident."

"Okay," he said. "What do you think about when you're confident?"

My mind went blank. I was hitting so poorly these last few weeks that I couldn't even relate to the question.

"I know you don't feel that way now," he coached patiently. "Take your time. Put yourself back at a time you hit with total confidence."

I watched our first hitter of the inning take a strike. Kovash was mowing. Things did not look good.

After a few moments my brain thawed enough to come up with a reasonable answer: "When I'm feeling confident I can't wait to hit again. I know I'm going to rip it and I imagine myself up there raking it."

"Does that thinking make you more confident or less?" the man asked.

"More confident."

"And that helps you hit better?"

"Yes, for sure."

"Do you remember last inning that I said you were asking for more bad hitting?" the man asked.

"Yes," I said, "not my favorite line of the day so far."

"Well let's just think about it," said the man, becoming more and more excited about his own ideas. I think he sensed he was getting my attention. "When you focus your energy on how badly you're hitting you feel bad, true?"

"True," I said.

"And then you go up and hit badly, true?"

"Pretty much, I guess."

"True or not true," the man pushed.

"True, yes, true," I said.

"Okay, then. That's my point. *Positive or negative, what you focus on, you feel. And how you feel largely determines how you play.* You follow that?"

"Yes."

"So when you're focusing your thoughts on something, you're asking for more of that something. Right now you're focusing on how badly you're hitting which makes you feel badly and then you go up and hit badly. So it's sort of like you're asking for it. That's why I'm saying: 'What you're focusing on you're asking for more of.'"

"Okay," I said. "But I struck out. Am I supposed to be happy about that? How am I supposed to feel good about that?"

"I'm not saying you should feel good about striking out," said the man, "that's a level of thinking well above where you are now. But there's no excuse for not making the effort to get yourself thinking in a way that will help you help your team.

Negative thinking is very selfish. It hurts the team because it hurts your performance.

Plus, you're spewing out all this negative energy which hurts your team's energy, too. Your team needs you right now and you're out here crying in your milk."

"That's easier said than done," I said. His last line cut me. I wanted to fight back, but I knew he was right. "I don't think I can be Mr. Happy right now."

"I hear you," he said. "You probably won't walk up there this next time feeling unstoppably confident, but let's get going now so you can start enjoying yourself and expanding yourself and getting into a position to help your team win."

I can't imagine any other circumstance where I'd let some guy I don't know and can't even see coach me during a game, much less a championship series game. But I was hurting and something about the guy felt good. For some reason I trusted him. *Do I know him?*

"I've gotta go," I said, realizing I was in the hole. But I'd like to pick this up later."

"Sure," the man said.

I hustled in toward the bat rack to get my weapon, hoping somehow things would be different this time.

Just as I grabbed my bat, Paul Solberg, our head coach, put his hand on my shoulder: "We're going to let Stock hit for you," he told me.

The bottom dropped out of my heart and landed in my gut with a thud.

I couldn't blame Solzy; I wasn't producing.

"I know you can hit. Oh, yep, yep, yep you can hit," Solzy said in his unique way *(is there something about becoming a coach that makes guys develop quirky aspects to their personalities?).* "I'm going to give Stock a chance to hit and play first a couple of innings. This way he gets to stay sharp if we need him tomorrow."

Part of me was relieved. I didn't have to go back out there feeling so bad. But I worried that I might end up sitting out tomorrow's game also. Was that part of "need him tomorrow"?

After high-fiving Stock and wishing him well, I grabbed some seeds and a cup of water and headed back out to the man. That was one plus of being pulled from the game: I had more time to talk to this guy. Maybe he could get me "big" by tomorrow.

PLAY BIG

Questions to Consider from Part 1:

1. What is the most important question in baseball?

2. What does the man mean by "baseball is a game of contrast?" Why must you fail to have fun?

3. What is the hidden cause of technical mistakes?

4. What is the REAL source of your results

5. Part 1 is called "Do You Make These Mistakes in Hitting and Pitching." What mistakes would you say 21 is making?

Are you a coach, teacher or serious player?

Print a FREE workbook and watch FREE PLAY BIG Training Videos at

www.PlayBigTraining.com

Part 2:

"Simple System Makes Playing with Confidence as Easy as ABC"

You're about to discover...

- **Where to go to get confidence FAST**

- **The key to consistently playing at or near your best**

- **Secrets to Hall-of-Fame mental preparation**

- **How to focus like a laser at the plate and on the mound**

- **How to regain your focus between pitches**

How to Get Confident Fast

When I got to the fence, I blurted out, "Don't tell me, you're going to say I was asking to come out of the game."

"I don't have to tell you," the man said wryly. "It's the Law."

"The law?"

"Yes, there's a law that makes everything that happens easy to understand. No time for that now, let's get going. Now we have some time to work. I've got a great exercise for you."

I wanted to come up close to the fence so I could see the guy better, but he was so close to the fence it would have been really weird for me to do it. I kept my manly distance and re-engaged in the conversation.

The man shifted into full coaching mode. I could feel his energy and enthusiasm rise.

"We've already decided that what you focus on you feel," he said.

"And what you focus on you attract more of. In fact, what you focus on you're asking for more of."

"Yes," I agreed, even though the "asking for more of" still seemed a stretch.

"So what do you think you should focus on to put yourself in the best possible shape to have a good at-bat this next time up?"

"Hitting well, I suppose."

"Yes," the man said, "and since you aren't exactly hitting well now…"

"Thank you," I interjected.

"…and then as you've said it's pretty hard to imagine hitting well in the future. So what's left?"

"The past?" I guessed.

"Exactly. Let's go back to a time when you felt totally and unstoppably confident. Can you think of a specific time when you felt that way?"

"Pretty much all last summer," I said, fondly recalling the days when I could hit. They seemed forever ago now, like it was someone else who got those hits. "At one point I was 50 for 101."

"Great," the man said, "but there's great power in being specific. Can you think of a specific game, even a specific at-bat, where you really felt unstoppably confident? You don't even have to have gotten a hit – you might have lined out or something – but just effortlessly pounded the ball."

"Well, actually, that's not too hard to come up with. One game pops right to mind," I said.

"Good, go with that. Get into the habit of paying attention to what pops into your mind. Your mind is showing you that for a reason. Now, give me a name for that time, like the team you were playing against or where the game was being played."

"It was on my Legion team, the Blues, and we were playing against Detroit Lakes, at their place, and the bases were loaded in the first inning. I had been…"

"Got it, got it," the man cut me off, "I don't need the details; just needed a name for it."

"Okay," I said, bummed I couldn't tell the whole story, "let's call it 'the DL game.'"

"Great. Turn so you're facing the field now, we don't want your teammates thinking you're not paying attention to the game. And please just do what I say."

I turned to face the field. We were back on defense. (Stock had grounded out, which didn't upset me at all. Not that I was rooting against him, of course, but I did want to play tomorrow.)

I stood evenly on both feet and committed to myself that I would do whatever this man said. He was right:

I needed to do something different or I was going to get the same results I'd been getting.

"Now take a deep breath into your belly, hold it for a moment, and let it go," the man said softly, confidently. "Relax."

It felt good to get some air down deep in me. Seemed like it had been awhile. I hadn't realized how little my breaths had been.

I took another deep, full breath... and felt my shoulders and (strangely) my hamstrings let go a little.

"Now go back to that time," the man continued, "that DL game, when you felt totally and unstoppably confident. See what you saw, hear what you heard, and begin to feel how good that feels to be totally confident, totally sure you will rip the baseball, totally certain you're the man."

His calm voice made the images come back quickly and clearly. Although my body was standing outside the dugout at Matson Field, the rest of me was on deck in DL with the bases about to load up in the first inning.

I could see the old wooden stands of the ballpark (they used to have a minor-league team in DL, like in the 1960s, and they had a classic covered grandstand). They even had a wooden outfield fence, like they do in the minor leagues, with old billboard ads lining the wall.

The light towers were classic: Giant, metal structures that rose up from the earth like monsters from a sci-fi movie. Each tower had four posts in a square at the bottom, and then crisscrossing steel bands rising up about 125 feet. With four of them in the outfield and two up each foul line, they had the field surrounded.

"See what you saw," repeated the man.

I saw the view from just outside our third-base dugout. I saw my parents and brother in the stands. They'd made the 45-minute road trip to watch me play.

As I strutted to the plate I saw the catcher and umpire waiting for me at the plate. I saw home plate and the right-handed batter's box ready to go. I saw my right foot clear the box and then find its place in the back of the box.

I saw the pitcher, a typical high school righty. He'd already given up two singles and a walk in the first and he didn't look too happy to see me come to the plate.

I, on the other hand, was quite happy to be there.

"Hear what you heard," said the man.

I heard my teammates cheering for me, clapping. I'd been on a tear lately and they could sense it was feeding time for the big dog. "Attention press box," one said loudly in a taunting, teasing tone, "prepare to change the score."

I sort of heard their coach and bench encouraging their pitcher, but really I mostly heard silence. I was so focused I could hear my spikes digging into the dirt around home plate.

"And feel how good that feels to be totally and unstoppably confident," continued the man.

My chest felt big and full. I could feel myself moving slowly, deliberately. I owned the batter's box. I'm King and this is my domain.

I felt a wry grin creep onto my face. I knew this guy couldn't handle me. I knew if he threw a strike he would be punished severely.

I love this feeling!

My mind jumped to the final pitch of the at-bat. I could see the ball tumbling out of his hand. I could see the spin (tumbling like clothes in a dryer). It was the meatiest curveball in the history of Minnesota baseball.

I felt myself wait on the ball. I felt myself staying back, loading, loading, watching, watching and BAM!! Powerfully yet effortlessly I crushed the ball. I love that feeling: Hitting a ball so cleanly, so squarely, with such a sweet stroke that I don't even feel the ball hit the bat.

I knew before I got out of the batter's box it was gone. Bomb to left-center. I'd only hit a handful of homers before that, but I knew it was gone.

The rocket/ball flew violently through the summer air and the world stopped to watch it.

The moment was too magical for the ball to simply land beyond the fence. It was hit too well to fall peacefully to the earth. And it didn't. It smashed viciously into the monster light tower.

It's one thing to hit a home run, but yet another to hit a grand slam, and yet another to have it hit something so hard it makes an even louder BANG hitting the light tower than it did off the bat.

Baseball's version of an in-your-face power slam dunk.

"Keep replaying that at bat, that stance, that swing over and over in your mind," the man continued, "that's it."

I gladly complied and started over with me walking to the plate.

"And notice," he said, "from zero to 10, how confident do you feel right now?"

I felt pretty good. Certainly a huge improvement from just two minutes ago. "I'd say seven or eight."

"Okay," he said, "do whatever you need to do to get to a nine or 10. Go back and see what you saw. Make those images brighter now, and bigger like you just went from a regular movie screen to an IMAX screen. Turn up the volume on the sounds, and let the feelings get even stronger."

I wasn't sure I could get myself to feel much better, but I was willing to give it a try.

"Give yourself permission to let go of whatever you're mentally holding on to. Give yourself permission to feel great."

I felt myself let go slightly, like when I'm stretching my hamstrings and they loosen and let me go a bit farther.

"And now physically show me what you looked like as you stepped into the box. Show me what your parents and teammates saw as you got into the box and get into your stance."

I stood up taller, took a full breath, and pretended to clear the batter's box with my right foot. I planted it firmly, put

my left foot down and started my pre-pitch movements forward and back. It felt good.

"Yes," he said, the enthusiasm and energy building in his voice, "see that pitcher out there."

I went into my stance and began to really rock forward and back, alternating each heel coming completely off the ground. I'd started doing that last winter after reading that Charlie Lau book. He said a good hitter has movement in his stance and I took it to an extreme. It had become my batting signature: rocking forward and lifting my back heel, rocking backward and lifting my front heel. Back and forth, back and forth in a menacing, "I'm-going-to-crush-this-ball-and-you-can't-stop-me" way. It was confident. It was arrogant. It was me at my best.

"10," I said. Going to IMAX, cranking the volume and actually moving my body the way I did when I was totally confident had pushed me over the top. I felt great. I felt strong. I felt confident. I felt like hitting.

I love this feeling!

"Keep replaying that moment, keep deepening that feeling," the man said. "And notice how you're acting. How are you moving? What's your posture like? Is your head more up or down? Shoulders back or forward? Are you moving fast or slow? With big movements or small?"

The answers to each question came immediately to mind, but he clearly didn't want me to answer out loud.

"Keep replaying the moment," he continued. "And now notice your breathing. What do you notice about your breathing? You may not have a strong sense of it in the moment, but tune into it now. Is it shallow or deep? Fast or slow? Simply notice what you notice about your breath.

"And finally notice what you're committed to. What are you focused on? What is your intent? What are you up there to do? What are you saying to yourself as you get into your stance?"

Wow, I said under my breath. *If you would have told me five minutes ago I'd be feeling this confident right now I would not have believed you.*

"Now I have some questions I want you to answer out loud," the man continued.

How to Make Playing Big as Easy as ABC

"What stands out to you the most about being a 10 in confidence?" the man asked.

"Well," I said, "I just felt so much more relaxed."

"Where in your body do you feel that relaxation?"

"All over," I said. "In my hands and in my legs. And I really noticed how much I was moving in my stance. I really rocked in my stance."

"Yes," said the man. "So you feel relaxed, particularly in your hands, and you're moving in your stance."

"Absolutely."

"I asked you about how you were acting, how you were moving, and your posture. What did you notice about those things?"

"I stood up tall. My head was up, my shoulders back. I felt like I sort of stuck my chest out. I was really relaxed, but, like, big."

"Anything else you notice about yourself physically?"

"I almost had a smile on my face. I just felt so good. I didn't break out into laughter, I was very focused and serious, but it was fun and I knew I was going to succeed and I had a little smile on my face. At least it felt like it."

"Nothing wrong with that," the man said. "Enjoyment is why you play. And if you play your best with a smile, then you should smile."

It was still hard for me to believe I felt good about my hitting.

"Okay, great," said the man. "So we'll say that's how you act when you're confident: head up, shoulders back, big chest, and even a slight smile. I'm going to make this as simple as possible. In fact I'll make it as easy as ABC. So the 'A' stands for Act Big. What does the 'A' stand for?"

"Act Big," I said confidently.

"Yes. If I only had one minute to coach you to feel better I'd spend most of that minute on acting confident.

It's much easier to feel confident by moving your body confidently than it is to create a feeling of confidence by just thinking differently."

That seemed odd to me, but I had just experienced it. When I started acting confident, like I did back in that DL game, I immediately felt better.

"Now the 'B' stands for Breathe Big. What does the 'B' stand for?"

"Breathe Big."

"What did you notice about your breathing when you were a 10 in confidence?"

"That's tougher to say," I responded. "I wasn't really that aware of it. But definitely slower than when I'm nervous. I just felt in control and everything, even the game, felt slower."

"Yes," said the man. "I try not to say there's a right answer to any of these questions. What's true for you is what's true for you.

But generally people feel more confident and more in control when their breathing is slow and deep."

"Yes," I said, "I'd say my breathing was deeper, like more into my gut than just up in the top part of my chest."

"Great," said the man, "so your 'B' is to Breathe Big, slowly and deeply."

"Got it."

"Now 'C' stands for Commit Big. What does..."

"Commit Big," I jumped in, recognizing the pattern.

"And that means going 'all in' with your focus on your target. Your full focus is committed to the ball or the mitt or whatever your target is. Your mind isn't split between a number of things, it's fully committed to one thing.

"What were you focused on during that at-bat in DL? What were you putting your energy into? What would you say you were committed to?"

"Really just seeing the ball and hitting it. I knew it would go and I'd be lying if I said I didn't think of hitting a homer, but I really wasn't thinking 'I gotta hit it,' or 'I gotta crush this pitch.' I was really just intent on seeing the ball and putting the fat part of the bat on it."

"And that's the target you were committed to," he said, "seeing the ball and putting the fat part of the bat on it."

"Big time."

I took a moment to reconnect with our game in front of me. I'd been so focused on the exercise that I'd lost track. Nothing had really changed. Evidently our whole team had pretty much lost track of the game.

Playing Big vs. Playing Small

Since our game was almost over, and I felt that I was gaining more confidence, I wanted to get a few more minutes with the man.

"Now, remember that I said we learn from contrast?" he said. "Let's look at the contrast between you when you're playing big and you when you're playing small. Tell me how your ABCs are different when you're hitting great and when you're slumping."

"Okay," I said. "When I'm hitting great, I Act Big. I stand up tall, big and move kinda slow and easy, maybe even smile. I relax my hands and move a lot in my stance. And when I'm slumping I'd say I get smaller. I hang my head and shoulders, look down a lot, and, now that I think about it, I really don't move much in my stance."

"So when you're in a slump your body does what?"

"Well, I guess it slumps."

"Yep. Might be where the term comes from."

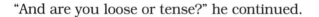

"Huh," I grunted, realizing that when I was in a slump I actually slump my body.

"And are you loose or tense?" he continued.

"Totally tense," I said. "I was pretty tight for that first at-bat today. I was jumpy. I didn't give myself a chance to see that curveball until it was too late. That doesn't happen much when I'm really confident."

"So you act pretty differently when you're hot versus when you're in a slump," the man summarized.

"Very."

"And B?" the man asked.

"Breathe Big," I said, taking a moment to feel my way to an answer. "Well, when I'm a 10 in confidence that's what I do: breathe deeply and slowly. And when I'm slumping I'd say my breathing is shallow and high. Like almost in my throat."

"Yes," said the man, "you literally choke."

"Maybe that's why they call it choking," I said, proud to have made that connection.

"I guess probably so," he said, tipping his head forward slightly in acknowledgement. "And how are your Cs different?"

> ## "When I'm feeling confident I'm all-in committed to just seeing the ball and putting the fat part of the bat on it.

"And when I'm slumping – wow – when I'm slumping all kinds of different things run through my head. Like today, how big this game is, how important it is for us to win so we don't have to face Kamin in a deciding game, how I haven't been hitting well, how my average is in the tank, and how I need to keep my front side closed, and...."

"Okay, Okay, stop, that's all I can take," laughed the man. "You're making me anxious. So the differences between you as a 10 and you in a slump in just your ABCs are pretty clear."

"Very much so," I said.

PLAYING BIG	Playing Small
Acting BIG: *Head up, chest up, SMILE!*	*Slumped:* *collapsed chest, sad face*
Breathing BIG: *Deep, Slow, Full.*	*Choking:* *shallow to no breath*
Committing BIG: *Fully focused on one target.*	*Fractured:* *lots of random thoughts*

"Now let me ask you this: Can you control whether you do your ABCs?"

"Well," I thought for a moment, "I guess so. I mean a few minutes ago I was feeling pretty badly, but then I was able to Act Big, Breathe Big, and Commit Big, so yes, you can control that."

"I agree," he said.

His next question was simple, but it ultimately completely changes the game of baseball.

What to Focus on to Maximize Your Success

The man continued with his questions. This time with one that's mind-boggling for baseball people.

"Can you control whether or not you get a hit?"
asked the man.

I was feeling good about my performance in our last exchange, so I dove right into this question. At first it seemed like another one of his lay ups, but it didn't turn out that way.

"Well, yes and no," I said. "If I go up there confident I'll get a hit and I swing at a good pitch with a good swing, yes. But other times I'd say no."

"So is it a yes or no?" said the man, again laughing at me.

"I guess I'd have to say 'no.'"

"I guess I'd have to agree," he said. "You can do everything right: go up there with confidence, get a good pitch to hit, swing with great mechanics, hit the ball squarely on the fat part of the bat, and line out before you even take two steps toward first base. It's just part of the game."

"Yes, one of my least favorite parts," I sighed. "I know I don't get a hit every time I walk up there confidently."

"This is one of the biggest traps players fall into. You only have so much mental energy to spend at any given moment, and it takes a lot of focus to play baseball well.

So if you spend energy on things you can't control it's a waste and it will lead to a lot of wasted at-bats."

"I hear that," I acknowledged.

"It happens to the best of them, and at every position. Pitchers think they should be able to control whether or not they get a batter out, but they can't. An umpire can make a 'bad' call, a fielder can make an error, or the hitter can bloop one between fielders. Sometimes batters even turn good pitches into missiles."

"I've hit some good pitches hard, I know that, especially when I'm hot. I'm sure the pitchers aren't happy about that."

"So you don't control your results and when you focus on things you can't control, your performance suffers. What do you think I'm going to suggest you do?"

"Focus on what I can control?"

"Yes. And you then you should immediately be asking 'How?' It's easy to say, 'focus on what you can control.' But it's like saying 'Don't try too hard, just go out and be yourself.' When you hear that you should say 'How?' How do I do that?'"

"Yeah, how do I do that?"

"Great question!" the man laughed. "But I already gave you the answer:

**Go out there and do your ABCs!
Remember them? They're your recipe
for success, your success system.**

You can control them and they give you your best chance for success. They don't guarantee success. They can't even guarantee you'll feel confident. But they give you your best chance. Just go out there and Act Big, Breathe Big, and Commit Big on every pitch with all your energy. No matter what."

I nodded in agreement and we watched a couple of pitches in silence. The only thing big in the game now for us was the Rakeops' lead. Barring a major rally, we were going to get Kamin in the deciding championship game.

"Okay," said the man, "you're ready for my quiz. What do you think you should focus on if you're two for your last 23?"

"Well," I paused.

"Come on, man," he said impatiently, "do your ABCs!"

"Oh, yeah," I said.

"And how about if you're four for your last five?"

"Your ABCs?" I said, pretty sure I saw the pattern.

"Of course! Why would you do anything differently? Your ABCs are what you do when you're at your best, when you're fully and authentically you. They're within your control. Almost nothing else in baseball is. Got it?"

"Got it," I said.

"We'll see," he challenged. "What would you tell a pitcher to do if he's just starting the game and a bit nervous?"

"His ABCs."

"How about if the umpire just squeezed him on what should have been a called strike three?"

"His ABCs."

"How about if he's ahead in the fifth inning and just needs three outs to be in position to get the win?"

"His ABCs."

"How about if you're hitting and the game is on the line?"

"My ABCs."

"I think you get it," he said.

"If you want to consistently play at or near your best you need to follow a system.

You need to have a set routine for what you do on each pitch. Most players say the mental game is the most important part of baseball but they completely leave their pre-pitch thoughts and actions to chance. They spend their energy worrying about things they can't control, like their stats, and then neglect the one thing they can control. Ultimately they let their pre-at-bat and pre-pitch actions be determined randomly: When they're feeling good they do the right things. But when they're feeling bad they do things that only make matters worse. They do things like thinking about how badly they're hitting."

"It's almost like they're asking for more bad results!" I chimed in, my mood continuing to lift.

"Yes!" he laughed, "Good one. Can you imagine someone doing that?"

"No," I smiled and shook my head, playing along. "Doesn't seem very smart. Seems like it would hurt the team too. Getting all negative on yourself is a pretty selfish thing to do."

"I totally agree," said the man.

With that, Gary Thielen, our leadoff hitter, popped up. A big comeback looked less and less likely.

"Okay," said the man, his pace quickening, "There are just 3 parts to what I call your Play Big Hitting Success System:

You want to have a Pre-at-bat Routine, a Green Light Routine, and a Yellow Light Routine. The key to each is to keep it simple. Everything you do will be based on what you did in that DL game."

"So they'll be based on my ABCs?"

"Exactly. You'll tweak and change your routines over time, but actually not all that much."

Prepare to Play Big: Your Pre-AB Routine

"For your Pre-at-bat Routine, you first need to pick a time when your at-bat starts.

"Too often players just go through the motions of getting ready to hit. They say they have a routine they do in the hole and on deck, and they have their special moves they make at the plate, but it's very rare when someone really does a great job of consistently getting ready to hit. Have you ever been at the plate with one strike before you really realized you were at the plate hitting?"

"For sure," I said.

"You're physically there, but not energetically there. You aren't present, in your body, the way you are when you're really on your game."

"I know that feeling. It's like my body sort of feels lighter, in a bad way, like I'm off balance somehow."

"Yes," the man said.

"And everything happens fast."

"Yes."

"And the ball looks small," I said.

"You got it. Your body is there but your energy is not. You aren't fully in your body."

"The lights are on but no one's home," I chuckled, amused at myself.

"So step one to avoid that," said the man, "and more importantly step one toward consistently giving yourself your best chance for a great AB, is making a very conscious, deliberate transition from not hitting into your at-bat. So you want to have a clear line, a clear action that starts the process. To keep it simple, choose either when you first touch your bat, or when you first touch your helmet."

"I'll say when I first touch my bat," I said.

 The PLAY BIG Success System

Once you know your Play Big ABC's, clarify and practice each of the following:

1. **Your Pre-AB (or pre-inning) Routine**
2. **Your Green Light Routine**
3. **Your Yellow Light Routine**

"Okay, so pause for a moment just before you touch your bat and run through your ABCs. Act Confident by lifting your head, shoulders and chest into your posture of confidence, take a nice deep breath, and tell yourself what you are going to do, like 'see the ball and put the fat part of the bat on it.' Then, if you feel ready, pick up your bat."

"I see," I said, "that makes sense."

"In time you can modify this and all other parts of your routine, but start with this."

"Will do."

"From then on," the man continued, "when you're in the hole and on-deck, simply repeat your ABCs. Do an impression of yourself in the hole and on deck at your DL game. Act the way you acted then, breathe the way you breathed, and commit to the target, commit to your simple plan for the at-bat."

"Got it," I said.

"In the hole, put particular focus on getting your body loose. When you're on deck, pretend you're up. You might even want to do your pre-pitch routine on a few pitches the pitcher throws to the guy before you. Maybe even each pitch."

"Okay."

"Move at the pace you hit best at – for many that means keeping it slow and controlled. Slow the game down by moving slowly and thinking clearly. Keep it simple. Lift your head and shoulders, take a deep breath, and allow your hands, shoulders, and legs to relax. Tune in to your body.

Notice how it feels. Make any adjustments to it you notice it needs to be as confident and relaxed and yet energized and focused as you can get at the moment."

"Got it."

"DON'T focus on trying to exactly create the feeling you had in DL. Use it as a guide, a direction to go, but this isn't about directly re-creating that. That was then. This is now. Create something new. Create a new great feeling.

"It will likely feel similar to the DL game and other great AB's you've had, but don't make the mistake of saying 'Oh, I can't get that in-the-zone feeling I had in DL, I'm doomed.' No, enjoy feeling good now. Enjoy what feeling as good as possible feels like now. Any energy you spend on how good you don't feel is energy wasted. Feel as good as you can right now and enjoy it."

"Cool," I said, "got it."

"There's lots of things I can teach you to help you feel better before you hit, but for now just focus on your ABCs."

Play Big This Pitch: How to Focus at the Plate with Your Green Light Routine

"Now, at the plate, you first have your Green Light Routine. That's what you do when you're feeling good. The intent of your pre-at-bat routine is to raise your vibration and get you focused."

"Raise my vibration?" I said.

"Never mind," he retracted, "we'll talk about that later. But you ought to come to the plate feeling pretty good thanks to your pre-at-bat efforts. Your Green Light Routine is based on your ABCs: at the plate you Act Big, Breathe Big, and Commit Big to your plan. And again the place to start is to simply do an impression of yourself at DL. Tell me what you did at the plate that day. No, show me and tell me."

"Okay," I said, pretending I was at home plate. "Acting Big, I walked up to the plate tall and big and pretty slow. Not rain-delay slow, but deliberate. I cleaned out the box with my right foot before digging that foot in near the back of the box 'til it felt good."

As requested, I was acting each move out as I said it.

"Then I stepped out and looked for signs from our coach at third," I continued. "Then I stepped back in with my right foot first, then my left."

"And in terms of your ABC's...?" the man said.

"I was Breathing Big — slowly and deeply. I may have even taken a big deep breath like you see them do on TV sometimes."

"Add that in for me now," he said, "take a deep breath as you position that front foot. Try inhaling as you lift your left from outside the box, and exhale as you put it down in your stance."

He coached me as I moved my feet and breath: "That's it. Slow and deliberate but powerful. In control. Totally free and relaxed. Good. You look great."

"I feel ready to hit," I said.

"And C?" he asked.

"Commit Big," I said softly, thinking of how I did that. "I was all in on just seeing the ball and hitting it. Like you said before, put the fat part of the bat on the ball."

"Great," he said, "say that now that you're in the box."

"See the ball," I said to myself, "fat part on it." I began rocking forward toward the pitcher and back, forward and back, feeling a nice rhythm.

"Great," he said. "How does that feel?"

"Big," I said, surprised at the enthusiasm in my voice. "Feels good. But I also know when I'm really hitting well I don't think about anything when I'm in the box. Now you're giving me stuff to think about."

"Yes, ideally when you're in the box your mind is free and clear. As long as you're focused on the ball, of course, and it's not the 'nobody home' syndrome we talked about a minute ago. But it's not easy to do. Try right now to think of nothing. And make sure you don't think about a pink elephant."

Doink! All the sudden a pink elephant appeared in my mind. "I can't do it," I said after just a few moments.

"Okay, then," he said, "the closest thing to nothing is one thing. So pick one thing to have as your last conscious thought before a pitch, and then let that thought fade into nothing. 'See the ball' is a good one, 'fat part of the bat on

the ball' is another. 'Right back at 'em' or 'see the ball, trust my hands' can work. You need to find what works for you at the moment. Find what puts your mind in the best position to trust and react.

"Say your word or phrase to yourself in the box in a way that helps you get ready, then let that thought fade into no thought as the pitcher gets things going."

"I see," I said.

"This way *instead of letting chance determine what you're thinking about and what you're focusing your energy on at the most critical moment, you're making a conscious, deliberate choice.*

"And again, you're keeping it..."

"Simple," I said.

"Right on. So that's your Green Light Routine."

Ping! The familiar sound of ball on metal bat turned our heads to the field. Kent Finanger had connected well, but in an instant it was clear he didn't get enough of it to change the score. The left fielder set up camp a few steps short of the warning track and the ball fell harmlessly into his glove.

The inning was over.

We were still down 8-2 with just one more turn at bat, but a part of me didn't mind. I wanted to play tomorrow. I wanted a chance to try out my Green Light Routine.

Yellow Light Routine: What to Do When You Lose Focus

"One last thing with your Play Big Success System and this first level of coaching," the man said. "It's called a Yellow Light Routine."

"I see a traffic light theme going here."

"Yes," said the man, rushed. "Think of each pitch in a game like an intersection when you're driving. If the light is green you just keep going. No problem, roll on through and keep doing what you're doing. But if the light is yellow, or of course red, you need to make a decision: 'Am I okay to go on as I am or do I need to stop?'"

"Or speed up," I quipped.

"That's what you did this last time up, how did that work for you?"

"Not good."

"No, that was a bad choice and you crashed and burned."

"Yep."

"Got it," I said.

"A yellow light is when you feel upset. You get angry, frustrated, nervous, tense, stuff like that..."

"Been there," I interrupted.

"So what I'm calling a green light is when you feel good between pitches. You're rolling, things are good. That's when you use your Green Light Routine. Your GLR helps you feel good and focused. But you use it when you feel pretty good already.

"... and you don't feel good. You don't feel right. You don't have a green light. You need to take some time to regroup. Just like you need to wait for a green light when you're driving, you need to get yourself back to 'green' before you go on with the next pitch.

"Actually, you walked up to the plate with a yellow light this last time, you didn't look confident. Your energy was off."

"I'd say I've been in a red light district for a couple of weeks now."

"Your Yellow Light Routine (YLR) is what you do when you feel something isn't right. You're distracted by something that happened, like a bad call by the umpire, a bad play by a teammate..."

"Or swinging at a bad pitch," I added.

"Or swinging at a bad pitch, right. The good news is that no matter how good you get at what I teach you will always have adversity in baseball."

"That's good news?"

Let your emotions be an "internal traffic light" directing your energy. Use your ABC's and Green Light Routine to generate a Green Light before you even take the field. Then recognize when you get a Yellow Light (you're upset or lose confidence) and use your Yellow Light Routine to get back to Green.

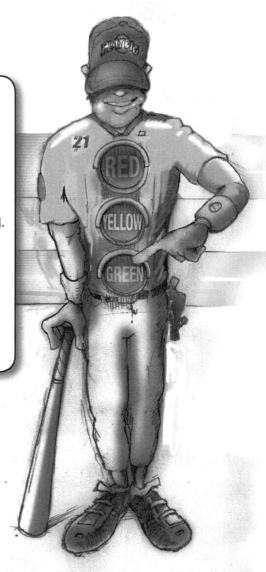

"Yes, remember that the challenges of baseball are the heart of what you enjoy about it. And they're the very things that compel you to expand yourself. So while with training the game will become easier, you don't ever beat the game of baseball. You never slay it and save the princess."

"Oh, yeah," I said, "I forgot that I love the failure. Now I guess I need to love yellow lights."

We watched Kovash get Swanson to chase a changeup.

"To finish up," said the man, "your YLR is simply to step back and take some extra time to go through your ABCs one more time. You just stop, step back, Act Big because when you get mad you contract and tighten; Breathe Big because when you get upset or nervous your breathing shallows or stops; and Commit Big because when you get negative you usually get distracted and lose your focus."

"Got it."

"The key, of course, is to recognize you have a yellow light. If you don't recognize it, if you don't see the yellow or red light, you roll straight through the intersection, or in this case, the pitch. Sometimes you'll make it through fine, but more often you'll get busted and play the pitch poorly."

"Makes sense," I said. "So I do my pre-at-bat routine to get a green light before I go to the plate?"

"Yes," said the man, "very good."

"And then I do my Green Light Routine at the plate."

"On each pitch," he added.

"On each pitch. And between each pitch I need to sort of check my traffic light to see if I'm green and okay to go, or if I'm yellow, meaning I'm upset or nervous about something. If I do get a yellow light, I need to step back, take some extra time, and do an extra round of my ABCs."

"You got it," said the man, "way to go! Now all you need is practice. You need to practice using your ABCs, doing drills so that they hold up when you're in a game situation. As I said, emotions are very powerful and when an emotional tsunami hits you get stupid really fast."

I nodded. I've gotten stupid fast, and stayed there long.

"So that's your first lesson in playing big: take your brain's reigns by *Acting Big, Breathing Big and Committing Big.* Commit to that process no matter what has happened or what might happen. That's the first level."

"First level... you mean there's more?"

"Yes, but..."

"Let's go, I want more."

There I was, lunging out for more coaching from this guy like it was one of Kovash's breaking balls. I should have guessed the man would throw me a curveball too, but I had no idea what was coming.

"No," said the man. "That's plenty for today. Tonight practice your Green and Yellow Light Routines so tomorrow you have a chance at executing them. Shift your focus now to doing your routines and away from getting hits. Focus on the process of hitting, not the outcome."

I was happy to have a sense of excitement after two weeks of hell. I felt clear on my homework, but not so clear on why this teacher had appeared.

"Mind if I ask why you're doing this?" I asked. "I don't know you, even though you certainly seem to know me. And obviously know what you're talking about."

"Well," said the man, pausing to consider his response. This was the first time he'd paused to think about what to say.

"Let's just say I can see a lot of myself in you."

"Yeah? How so?"

"I was a pretty good player in my day. No Babe Ruth, but not bad. But I couldn't get my head on straight. I got upset when I didn't do well. I got frustrated easily. I often felt like I needed to be perfect, yet I certainly didn't practice hard enough to find out how good I could be."

"That answers how you see yourself in me," I said.

"When I hung up my cleats for good I couldn't hang up the frustration. Why did that happen to me? Why couldn't I play as well as I knew I could? Why did I end up so far below my potential?

I felt like I'd wasted my one chance to play by not focusing on the mental game.

"Everyone always says it's the most important part of the game but so few players or even coaches give it the attention it deserves. So millions of players at all levels fall short of the enjoyment and expansion the game is offering them."

"I see. I'd say I'm on that path."

"Yes. It left a hole in my gut, a feeling of regret that took me a long time to let go. I committed myself to discovering the fastest and easiest way to help players have fun and grow as people. I've learned a lot. I like to watch games and when I see someone I think would be open to the coaching and might need the coaching, I invite them in."

"That's cool," I said. "Strangely, I'm glad you saw that in me. I'm definitely glad I accepted your invitation."

"Me too," the man said.

Ping! Our heads turned to watch the ball fly off of Dotseth's bat with some juice into center field, but it was right at their center fielder who caught the ball for the game's final out.

The stage was set: A full summer of baseball comes down to one game. I was amazed that I'd started the game feeling so terribly, but now I was excited to play tomorrow. I wanted to use my Pre-AB Routine, my Green Light Routine and, if needed, my Yellow Light Routine.

I just hoped I'd have the chance.

Questions to Consider for Part 2:

1. Where can you "go" to get confidence FAST?

2. What is the key to consistently playing at or near your best?

3. What is a Green Light Routine and when do you use it?

4. What is a Yellow Light Routine and when do you use it?

5. Choose an idea from Part 2 and imagine yourself using it in a game. Describe what you see, hear and feel when you imagine it.

I'll take you through the same "ABC" exercise "21" just went through in a FREE VIDEO at www.PlayBigTraining.com

Got an Organization You'd Like to PLAY BIG?

Bring **Dr. Tom Hanson** in to speak!

His dynamic, interactive style brings home the life-changing principles in this book.

For business groups Hanson blends his extensive experience coaching top executive and sales people to breakthrough results with engaging stories from baseball greats to create a memorable, performance enhancing experience.

For more information, write his office at
info@PlayBigTraining.com or call **813-968-8863**

Also check out the business coaching site:

www.HeadsUpPerformance.com

Part 3:

"The Mystery of Performance Breakthroughs, Solved"

You're about to discover...

- **How to Play Big on defense**
- **How to recover from failure**
- **The simple thing great players are great at (and you are probably not)**
- **Why complexity is vital to simplicity**
- **The single most important thing needed for a major performance upgrade**
- **The 2 things you MUST understand to breakthrough to the next level**

Find out at:

PlayBigBaseball.com

Preparing for the Big Game

I practiced my ABCs and Green and Yellow Light Routines at home that night and the next morning, and imagined doing them against Kamin in our final game.

The day dragged on forever. I watched SportsCenter a few hundred times while keeping one eye on the creeping clock.

Would I get to play? If I did, would I hit the ball?

I got to the park early, as did pretty much everyone else. Dots was almost late, he's slow at pretty much everything he does except swing a bat. We didn't take batting practice on the field, just in the cages up the right-field line, so everyone was just milling about doing baseball things.

I looked around to see if I could see the man who coached me yesterday, then laughed to myself that I wouldn't know him if I did see him.

I acted casual about making my way to the front of the dugout to see the lineup. Solzy always posted it there as soon as he had it. It was a summer league so it was often pretty laid back and the line-up would sometimes change late when someone couldn't make it. But there was nothing laid back about today. I could see as I entered the dugout from the outfield side the line-up was posted.

I put my shoes on and chatted with a couple of guys, pretending to be paying attention to what they were saying.

I did hear that we won a coin toss and would be home team again today. I then took a breath and strolled to the end of the dugout to meet my destiny.

6) Hanson, 3.

I was in! Starting at first base. Bumped one spot to hit sixth, but who cares? I was playing.

"I believe in you," said Solzy behind me, startling me slightly. He knew I'd be anxious about whether or not I'd play.

"Thanks, coach," I said. "I won't let you down."

"Yep, yep, yep," he said as I headed out to right field to stretch.

Game 3 drew a bigger crowd and more good weather. It's not too often around these parts that the weather is a non-issue three days in a row. But another sunny, billowy clouded day would be perfect for the big game.

Although I didn't have a hit in the series and we were facing an unbeaten pitcher, I actually felt pretty good about things as I laid back in the lush green grass loosening my quads.

I had no idea how much I was about to be stretched.

How to Play Big
on Defense

Game time finally came. Shortly before I trotted out to first base I looked to the left of our dugout to see if the man was

there. Sure enough, I could see that now familiar shadowy shape behind the wind screen. I stopped and called out to him.

"Great to sort of see you," I said with a smile.

"You too. Do your ABCs on defense while you're out there," the man said, not wasting any time. "They work out there too. Every pitch think, 'hit it to me.'"

"Will do," I said. "I'll bet you'd say the same thing to me if I were a pitcher."

"Absolutely."

"Good thing I won't have to worry about that," I laughed as our defense hustled onto the field.

"Worrying solves nothing anyway," he said, loud enough for me to hear as I reached my spot at first base.

Good grief! I thought to myself, *"This guy's relentless."*

I had a bounce in my step as I made the short trek to first base. I'd soon get to try out my new approach.

I felt noticeably different in the field. I stood tall, took a breath before each pitch, and focused on the ball on each pitch.

I was always pretty confident in my defense, but I really felt myself wanting the ball hit to me. I also found myself chattering support for our pitcher and even joking a bit with Joe Knight at second.

Hit it to me I said under my breath with each pitch.

Perhaps what I noticed most was the contrast of how I was being out there this inning compared to yesterday. I thought I'd done a good job of not bringing my failures at the plate out to the field with me, but apparently I hadn't. It felt great to feel good.

The first inning went quickly for both sides. This was not good. Kamin had only been vulnerable in the early innings of most games, so when he mowed us down in the first it was a buzz kill.

But Mike Dorigan, our pitcher, was looking good. He whiffed the Rakeops' six-hole hitter for the third out in the second inning and as soon as that ball hit Johnny Waddle's glove I ran to our dugout, determined to turn around my fortunes at the plate.

Playing Bigger
Between the Lines

"Do my ABCs, do my ABCs," I repeated to myself as I trotted in, "just like DL."

As was our custom, I got the ball I'd use to warm up my infielders the next inning from Jeffy Sklar and put my glove and hat on the top step of the dugout. My plan was to either have someone else bring my glove out to me because I was on base, or pick it up myself after I'd scored a run.

I grabbed my bat and said, "Let's go, boys" to Swense and Dots. I wanted to support them but also to let off some of the adrenaline building inside me.

"Right on," they said, "let's get this guy."

As I reached for my helmet I remembered my conversation with the man.

Oops, I said to myself, forgot to do the first thing he said!

Wow, I thought, things had speeded up on me just from the time I got back into the dugout before I could even get my bat in my hands. I'd never really noticed my thoughts and feelings like this before. How many ABs have I given away by not paying attention to my thoughts and feelings?

I put my bat back down in the rack and pressed up and out through the top of my head, lifted my chest and shoulders and took a deep breath into my belly.

"See the ball and put the fat part on it," I whispered to myself as I exhaled. My energy calmed and my pace eased. "Slow and steady," I said to myself as I grabbed my bat, "just like DL."

I felt much better.

I stepped out of the dugout and got clear of Dots and anyone else so I could swing my bat safely. In the hole, focus on getting your body loose, I remembered the man saying.

I transported myself back to DL as I swung and stretched. I could feel that sensation of confidence building. I still felt nervous and a bit tingly with anxiousness, but I could sense the positive energy starting to overcome the fear of yet another terrible at-bat.

Swense grounded sharply to short, and Dots, hitting in my old fifth spot, lined to first. My heart rate shot up instantly

when the ball popped the first baseman's glove. Time to play big.

I strode to the plate deliberately and confidently. My head held high and my chest open, I knew I wasn't anywhere close to as confident as I was at DL. But I walked like I was a good hitter, I breathed like I was a good hitter, and I was focused on my simple plan.

I was in control. I cleared out the right-handed batter's box with my right foot, dug it in until it felt secure, and then stepped out for a courtesy check of Bucky Burgau, our third base coach.

Nothing on.

So I went right into my Green Light Routine: Placed my back foot deliberately, took a nice breath into my belly (actually it was more like my chest – I was too amped up to get it all the way to my belly) and exhaled as I placed my left foot in the box.

I rocked toward and away from the pitcher and said to myself, "See the ball, fat part of the bat on the ball," twice before my hands came to rest near my right shoulder in my stance. I continued to rock forward and back, forward and back as Kamin went into his delivery.

I felt myself coil back as Kamin drew the ball back, then stride forward mirroring Kamin's move toward me. I saw the ball pretty well; "FASTBALL!" said my eyes as the ball screamed toward me. "INSIDE!"

I took it for ball one.

"Good one," I said to myself. "This feels okay. I can do this. I'll get this guy. Make him come to me."

I stepped out and again glanced at Bucky, but I knew nothing was on. I stood up and took a breath outside the box. It felt good. I noticed I'd picked up some tension on that swing and the breath let some of it go.

Green Light Routine. I confidently placed my right foot in its home in the back of the box. I paused a moment to check my posture to make sure I was acting confident. I adjusted my shoulders back to open up my chest more and then started to inhale. I placed my front foot down as I exhaled. *See the ball, fat part of the bat on it.*

Things felt even better now. I'd slowed it down. I felt more in control. See the ball. I rocked forward and back, forward and back, then coiled as Kamin went into his delivery....

"Fast B... CURVE!"

That familiar clothes-tumbling-in-a-dryer image filled my head. The pitch was going to be a foot outside.

"NO!" was the command sent from my brain, but before it could get to its destination my hips and hands had aggressively started forward. I slammed on the brakes, but my hands and bat skidded right over the plate before being yanked back toward the catcher.

"Yes he did!" came the cries from the Rakeops' bench.

But the home plate umpire needed no help. His right hand pointed at me and then to the air: strike one.

Arrrgh! I screamed silently at myself. *How many times do I have to see that before I get that tumbling ball means curveball you idiot!?*

Black ink pulsed through my veins. *Dog gone it! See the dang ball! How hard can it be?!*

Now the count was 1 and 1. *Shoot, I could have been ahead 2 and 0 and really sat on something to drive.*

I stepped out and took a few slow swings. "Come on, Hanny, you're alright," came the support from my dugout. "See that ball! You'll get him!"

As I stepped back in the box I thought *"Okay, fastball or curve this time? I can get it. I'm going to pound this pitch."*

As I came into my stance Kamin looked very different this time. He seemed closer and he was moving faster. I nervously swayed my bat back and forth over the plate a few times and settled into my set position.

Kamin rocked back and fired.

It was a ...... CURVEBALL! I saw it earlier this time, but I was so wound up my timing was still set for a fastball: I was out in front of the pitch again. My front side pulled open, but I was on it enough to hit it. My butt popped back toward the third base dugout as I reached for the ball.

Ping.

The ball hit the bat, but it would be a stretch to say the bat really hit the ball. I had been so out in front with my body and front side I had nothing left on the swing. The ball drifted

to right field in slow motion. One of the Top 10 Laziest Fly Balls ever. Actually, I'd call it sleepy.

The right fielder literally started walking toward the infield, appearing to me to be laughing at how easy a play he had to make.

My head was down well before I touched first base. *Dog gone it! Another bad AB.*

As I walked toward our dugout I could feel the man's presence behind the screen. "That helped a lot," I said to myself, sarcastically noting that even the Great ABCs couldn't buy me a hit.

I never looked over at the man. I wanted to launch my helmet over the dugout, but at least I maintained my dignity enough to not embarrass myself with that stunt.

Joe Knight brought my glove and ball out to me.

"It's alright, man, you'll get him. A lot of game left," he said.

But his well wishes bounced off my wall of anger. I would have none of it.

"Why am I So Bad?"

Throwing the warm up ground balls to the other infielders gave me a chance to unwind. I was glad to have a chance to play defense and not to be the designated hitter. It would not have been healthy for me to have to sit in there and baste in my negativity until I hit again.

I whipped the ball at the infielders pretty hard, letting go of some of my emotion with each throw.

I began replaying the at-bat in my mind. What had happened? I felt so good for one pitch, and then it all fell apart.

The man's lessons started their way across my mind. I did my Green Light Routine on the first pitch. I did it on the second. But then I swung at that curveball and everything fell apart.

I looked over at the man behind the screen. He was still just a dark shadow behind a thin wall of green. He stood there, no doubt looking at me. As I looked away I realized I could almost feel warmth from him. A supporting energy or something.

Who is this guy?

As my head continued to clear I started to look forward to hearing what he had to say about my latest failure.

How to Recover Between Pitches

After three quick outs, I put my glove in its familiar spot on the dugout steps and then headed toward my shadowy new friend.

"What did you notice?" said the man as I got closer to him.

"That's my question for you," I said. I had a bit of an edge but he'd earned my respect so I wasn't a jerk about it.

"You first," he said. "You're the one out there playing so you're the one who needs to know what happened."

"I actually felt good going up there. I did my pre-at-bat ABCs and did my Green Light Routine and saw that first pitch really well."

"Great," said the man. "I could see you doing it. You looked like a different hitter than your ABs yesterday. Then what happened?"

"I swung at that curveball. I can't believe I fell for that! Then I guess I got mad at myself and that was it."

"Well," laughed the man, "was your AB literally over after you swung at the curveball?"

"No."

"That only made the count 1-1, right?"

"Yes," I said. "But I was so mad at myself I guess I lost it."

"I guess. How was your Green Light Routine on that last pitch?"

I replayed the scene as best I could in my mind.

"I don't remember. Okay, I guess."

"Guess again. You didn't do it. You stepped out, took a few swings and hurriedly got back in the box. No acting big – you

got small, no big breath, no appearance of a commitment to a simple target."

"Oh," I said, sheepishly. "Things *did* seem to happen pretty fast."

"Yep," said the man. "But that happens with guys even after they practice their routines. You actually did great to remember it on the two pitches considering you just learned this yesterday. As simple as it sounds, this isn't something you just start doing out of nowhere. You need to practice it. It's not too tough to do it standing here by the dugout. It's a whole other ball game when you step out between those white lines."

"That's for sure," I said.

"Your energy was good on the first two pitches, but then when you took that check swing at the curveball you got mad at yourself. That was a yellow light."

"More like a red light," I said.

"I agree. And yet instead of stepping back and taking extra time and taking any actions to get yourself back to green, you gunned it right through the intersection — the next pitch."

"I see," I nodded. "It was time for a Yellow Light Routine."

"Very good," said the man. "Yes, your ABCs are always there to come to your aid."

"I should have thought of that. I guess I just lost it and forgot."

"That's the way it goes," said the man. "When we get flood-ed with emotions they wipe away our untrained intentions. That's why I was impressed that you were even able to stay with your pre-at-bat and Green Light Routines as long as you did."

"That's cool, I guess, thank you."

Our half of the inning ended quickly and our team was heading back onto the field.

"So that's it," said the man with a sense of finality. "You've got your ABCs and Green and Yellow Light Routines. That's all you need. You just need to practice them."

"Wait a minute," I said anxiously, fearing I was about to lose the man's help, but needing to get back to my spot at first base. "You said they were just level one, that there's much more you can teach me."

"Indeed there is," he said, "there's much more powerful knowledge and skills on the next level."

"Come on," I pleaded, "you can't leave me hanging. Sounds like you've held back your best stuff."

"Go play defense. While you're out there I'll feel into whether I think it's a good idea to take you there right now."

Great Players are Great at This Simple Thing

After another 1-2-3 inning I was promptly back at the fence.

"Let's go," I said, "level two."

"Okay, 21," said the man. "I can feel your eagerness and I'm willing to take you further. But I'm warning you, once I reveal these secrets to you there's no going back. You can choose not to follow what I say, but deep down you'll always know whether or not you're living your truth."

"I hear ya," I said. But the voice in my head said: *living my truth? How did we go from hitting to living my truth?*

"You don't need any more: Just practicing and doing your ABCs on each pitch will help you enormously. They are enough."

"No, no," I said. "I like the ABCs, but I definitely want more. They actually seem too simple."

"Simple wins, 21," said the man. "Keeping it simple isn't just smart, it's genius. Talk to any great hitter and he'll tell you that. Ask Hank Aaron what he was doing at the plate and he'll tell you 'I just wanted to put the fat part of the bat on the ball.' And ask Stan Musial, lifetime .331 hitter, what he was doing and he'll tell you 'I always knew where the fat part of the bat was and I wanted to put it on the ball.' Rocket science? I don't think so."

I made a mental note to ask those and other great hitters what they were thinking; I wanted to hear that for myself.

The man continued: "Any time you or anyone else, pitcher or hitter, is playing well they'll tell you they're keeping it simple. 'It's just me and my target,' a pitcher will say, 'I just focus and let it fly.'

"And any time you or someone else, pitcher or hitter, is playing poorly they will tell you things have gotten complicated. They're thinking about their mechanics – like 'keep my hands back,' 'keep my elbow up,' or 'fire my hips' – or they're worried about the future – like 'I gotta get a hit.'"

"Or," I chimed in, "like me they're focused on the past, on how badly they've been hitting."

"Exactly," said the man. "But hear this, because this is vitally important to success in baseball or anything else:

The REAL power of simplicity comes when you've gone through some complexity to get there."

"Huh?"

"Look at your ABCs. Pretty simple, right? Act Big, Breathe Big, Commit Big."

"Yes."

"And powerful, right?" he said. "You really feel the power of that, yes?"

"I do, yes, no question."

"But if I would have just said to you, back when you were all upset, if I'd have said, '21, you just need to Act Big, Breathe Big and Commit Big' would that have helped you?"

"Honestly, probably not."

"Right. You were too upset for one, but the words had very little meaning to you. What gave the ABCs their real power for you?"

"I guess going through the exercise we did. Going back and re-experiencing that time when I really felt confident in the DL game."

"Yes!" the man exclaimed. "By going through what I'll call the *complexity* of that exercise, by you deeply and person-ally experiencing Acting Big, Breathing Big and Committing Big, those words took on a whole new meaning for you. So now my saying, 'Go out and do your ABCs' is both simple and powerful for you."

"I get it," I said.

"If you went into that dugout and told your pitcher he needs to Act Big, Breathe Big and Commit Big he'd probably look at you kind of funny. Those words make sense, but they have a whole different meaning for you because of the expe-rience you went through."

"I see," I said, "that makes sense."

"It's sort of like if you walk up there your next at-bat and step on home plate it would mean nothing. No

one would say a word. But if you hit the ball and run safely around the bases and THEN step on home plate it would have huge meaning and your dugout would be jumping up and down.

"Both times you just stepped on home plate – very simple. But because of what you went through before each time they each had very different meanings."

"Okay, got it," I said, starting to get impatient, "I'm ready to go on, where is this going?"

"I'm about to get into some stuff that will stretch your mind a little."

"Okay," I said, shifting to a growing sense of excitement with a dash of nervousness.

"But in the end it will, just like the ABCs, come back to some very simple things."

"But that simplicity," I said with some pride, "will have a lot of meaning because of the complexity you're going to take me through."

"You're a smart rat," the man said in a tone that I could tell he had a big grin on his face. "If you stick with me I'll give you a simple way to consistently play at or near your best. I'll give you a way to feel more confident any time you want; overcome the frustration the game throws at you; and play with freedom – the ultimate prize.

"In the end what to do will be profoundly simple – But also amazingly powerful."

"I'm all in."

"Okay, hold on, 21, you're about to go on a wild ride. We may even be able to get it done in time for you to help your team win this game."

All Major Performance Upgrades are the Result of Major Thinking Upgrades

The man shifted into high gear. I could feel his passion building: "All major performance upgrades are created by major thinking upgrades. Not just superficial, think-a-lit-tle-more-positive-and-see-things-bit differently thinking. But, rather, deep, fundamental shifts in worldview."

I prepared myself to go deep on this one (it would be nice to go deep on *something*).

"Back in the day," the man continued, "people thought everything revolved around them, including the sun. Any idiot could see the sun moved across the sky, right?"

"Well..." I stammered.

"Right!" said the man, clearly getting fired up. "Imagine what that was like. For centuries it was so obvious that the sun was doing the moving no one even questioned it. Then all of the sudden this mind-blowing change!"

"I'm sure," I said, still trying to grasp how preparation for my next at-bat had its roots in world history.

"My point is this: Taking a quantum leap in your baseball performance requires more than a little tweak to your thinking."

"It takes a big shift," I said.

"Yes. For most players, just getting into the mental aspects of the game, like learning my ABCs is a big paradigm shift.

"Cool," I said, my mind starting to spin as the conversation broadened. "But I want to win this game. Will it help me do that?"

"Absolutely," the man said. "I wouldn't get into it with you now if it wouldn't. But we need to move right along because I need to ease you into it."

"Fire away," I said.

Two Things You Must Understand to Break Through to the Next Level

"Our first step is to look more closely at two things," the man began. "You need to look at one, the nature of the universe, and two, the nature of humans, how humans are designed."

"Sheesh," I said, "you don't mess around. Those are big league topics."

"Indeed. *The higher the level of thinking you challenge the bigger the payoff.* If you want to make big changes in your game, you need to look at fundamental assumptions you're making about how things are. All the big paradigm shifts we talked about that led to major 'performance' improvements came from challenging very basic assumptions: the sun revolves around the Earth, the Earth is flat, and so on."

"Got it," I said.

"The funny thing is these major breakthroughs are simply the result of seeing reality more clearly. It isn't that Columbus or Copernicus created anything new, they didn't invent anything. *They just more accurately saw what was already there.*"

"And Newton?"

"Didn't invent gravity, he just saw it more clearly than people before him. In order for you to make a huge leap in your performance, in your *enjoyment* and *expansion* as a person – you'll recall that's why I say you play baseball."

"Yes."

"In order to make major performance improvements we have to look closer and see more clearly the nature of the world we live in, including what it's made of and what laws control what happens."

"Like the Law of Gravity?"

"Yes," said the man. "There's a law governing what's happening in this game that no one is consciously aware of. I think you'll get a kick out of it. And like these other paradigm shifts I'm not going to invent anything, I'm just going to help you see 'reality' more clearly. That will give you more power to create the baseball career – and life – you want."

"Cool," I said. "What is this law that no one knows?" I asked.

"I'll tell you shortly. I first want to tell you a story."

Questions to Consider for Part 3:

1. How do you Play Big on defense?

2. What is the simple thing great players are great at (and you are probably not)?

3. Why is complexity so important to simplicity?

4. What is the single most important thing needed for a major performance upgrade?

5. What are the 2 things you MUST understand to breakthrough to the next level?

Get bonus content not included in the book, plus videos and a companion workbook all FREE at www.PlayBigTraining.com

Are YOU Ready to
PLAY BIG?

Come now to

www.PlayBigTraining.com

and get all this training *FREE!* *($150 VALUE)*

1. **The "ABC" Exercise**

2. **A workbook to deepen your learning**

3. **"Feel Good and Focus Chart" downloads**

4. **Unpublished book excerpts**

5. **Tapping Video to Remove Stress and Fear**

All the knowledge in this book will go to waste if you don't take action. All great players have coaches. Get yours now FREE at

www.PlayBigTraining.com

Try tapping yourself now *FREE!*

To make sure you do it right, tap along with me on a FREE VIDEO at

www.PlayBigTraining.com

©2011 Dr. Tom Hanson

"Going from thinking confidence is a random thing over which you have no control to realizing you can create a feeling of confidence when you want – especially if you practice – is a huge leap. Add realizing you can only control yourself, you can't control your results, and you've got the makings of a significant upgrade."

"I hear you," I said.

"But just hearing those things isn't enough, as I've said. You need to practice them and build up the 'muscles' that hold those beliefs in place."

"I hear you there, too."

"But what I'm going to tell you, in fact show you, is bigger and more fundamental than that. It's the next level. I've got a totally different way of looking at the game that will rock your world the way the major breakthroughs in thinking we mentioned rocked those people's worlds throughout history."

"Rock me!" I said, my enthusiasm was building, too.

"If you buy into it I promise it will simplify everything. It will make the game easier and more fun. And although we'll focus on baseball, this is really a different way to look at your whole life that will put you in the driver's seat to enjoyment and expansion. In fact, I'm about to share with you the simplest path to having a great life."

Part 4:

"Knowing This Fact, Discovered by Scientists Last Century, Gives You an Almost Unfair Advantage over Other Players and Coaches"

You're about to discover...

- What you must learn from a 19th century physician

- The field you are REALLY playing on ("21" had to see this fact to believe it)

- How to know when you're about to play small (and how to avoid it)

- The built-in device you already have that will guide you to high-level performance
(but you're probably trying to ignore it)

The Germination of Baseball Greatness

Strangely, the game seemed to have slowed down. Did this guy have a pause button or something he could press that allowed us the time we needed to talk? Or was it just me?

Frankly, I didn't care. I just wanted to know what the man would say next.

"Have you ever heard of Ignaz Semmelweis?" he asked.

"Did he play for the Brewers?"

"No," chuckled the man, "he was head teacher and surgeon of Vienna General Hospital in the 1840s."

"Sorry. I'm not strong on my 19th century physicians."

"Well, this is a good one to know. His story will tie in to yours soon."

It felt like the man was preparing me for something – like when a girlfriend is getting ready to tell you she just wants to be friends – but I had no idea what he had in mind.

"Okay, I'm in, tell me about the doctor," I said.

"Semmelweis had a horrible problem: nearly 20 percent of all women who came to him to give birth ended up dying."

"That's not good."

"No. His reputation was so bad that often when women in labor realized they were going to get his 'help' they instead gave birth to their babies on the street outside the hospital."

"Wow. I'm sure he felt good about that," I said sarcastically.

"Meanwhile, on the other side of the hospital where midwives delivered babies, only four percent of the moms were dying. The two sides of the hospital alternated days: one day the deliveries would be done by Semmelweis and his team, and the other day the midwives would do the deliveries. Needless to say, Semmelweis was pretty upset and confused by this."

"I'm sure," I said, now drawn in to the mystery. "What was the difference?"

"That's what Semmelweis asked. He tried everything he could think of: he changed the lighting, the number of people in the room, even the religious rites that were practiced in the room. But nothing helped."

"Then one day a medical student accidently cut another doctor with a scalpel the student had just used to cut up a dead body. The doctor fell ill and died days later."

"I wonder how killing your teacher affects your grade," I mused. "I've got one I'd like to..."

"Semmelweis did an autopsy on the doctor and found the same goop he saw in the dead mothers," the man pressed on. "He guessed there *must be something on the scalpels from the dead people that infects living people.*"

"Genius," I said.

"So he started a practice of having doctors wash their hands after working with cadavers before working on living mothers. And what do you think happened?"

"Fewer moms died."

"The death rate on his side of the hospital went down to below one percent. He had the midwives do the same thing and their mortality rate dropped too."

"That's great," I said, "but it seems pretty obvious. Any 5-year-old will tell you to wash your hands to get the germs off."

"Yes," said the man, "common knowledge and practice now. But back then they didn't know about germs. They couldn't see them, so they made up other explanations for why people got sick based on their own beliefs.

"This was in the time before they 'discovered' germs.

People didn't consider that something they couldn't see could have such a huge affect on their lives.

In fact, Semmelweis dedicated the rest of his life to convincing the rest of Europe's doctors that washing your hands and equipment before sticking them into a living body was a good idea."

"Cool," I said, "he must have become a big hero."

"No!" the man burst out, "he didn't."

"Why not?"

"Almost no one believed him!"

"What do you mean?"

"Doctors around Europe said, 'You're out of your mind, Semmelweis! There's no way washing your hands after working on a cadaver could in any way make it safer to stick your hands inside a living mother.'"

"Even with those death rate stats?" I puzzled.

"Even with those death rate stats. Semmelweis literally went crazy trying to prove his discovery and died of a funky brain issue at 47 having not convinced the general population of doctors that washing your hands was a good idea."

"Wow," I said, "that's a pretty crazy story. I guess if they're stuck in one way of thinking it's hard to switch."

"Yep," said the man.

"It isn't easy to convince people of something they can't see. People get stuck in their paradigms and it takes overwhelming evidence and time or a very powerful experience to change their minds.

"We already mentioned a few of the major paradigm shifts throughout history."

"Yes, I'm sure the whole 'flat world vs. round world' thing was a tough sell."

"Very," said the man.

"I also like the story I read about the 4-minute mile," I said, "how before Roger Bannister ran a sub-4-minute mile scientists thought it was impossible and that a human would likely explode if he ran that fast. Then, after Bannister did it, something crazy like 52 people did it in the next year."

"Yes, and only a couple of those guys blew up," the man cracked. "And did you know that in the late 1800s physics experts said there was no more need for physics Ph.D.s because everything there was to know about matter was already known?"

"No, that's a good one."

"Yes, since then Newtonian physics gave way to quantum physics, and the incredible revelation that everything in the universe is... well, I'm going to let you find out for yourself."

"Um," I said, "okay."

"A big difference between Semmelweis and the people he was trying to convince," said the man, "was his direct experience with the deaths and then the non-deaths. His direct experience made him more passionate and much more committed than any of the other doctors. Just like your direct experience with the ABCs makes you much more passionate and committed to using them."

"Yes."

"The doctors of the time believed they were the smartest guys in the room and had a lot invested in their ideas about health. The discovery of germs was a major breakthrough that radically changed how medicine was done. A lot of common practices were exposed as ineffective and a lot of doctors had to change or get left behind. As you'd expect, the younger doctors bought in to the idea of germs faster and easier than the older doctors."

"Yes," I said, "I know a couple of coaches like that."

"What do you mean?" the man said, testing my application of the idea.

"They just seem stuck in their ways. Like once they decide you're good they play you all the time no matter how you play. And once they decide you're no good you can never change their minds."

"Yes, good one. We'll talk more about coaches later," said the man. "But right now I want to give you another direct experience that will change YOUR mind pretty quickly."

"Oh?"

Although it was like watching a shadow, I could see the man bend over and pick up a small bag he had next to him and reach inside.

"You know how Semmelweis determined there must be something so small he couldn't see it being transferred from the dead people to the living ones?" said the man, standing with the mysterious object in his hand that was going to

give me some mind-blowing direct experience.

"Yes," I said, "and it turned the living ones into dead ones."

"Yes. And how once he discovered it he did a few simple things that made a dramatic improvement in his performance?"

"Yes. Wash hands, save lives. Pretty simple."

"What if there was an unseen force operating that was secretly influencing baseball the way germs influence our health? And what if you could, like Semmelweis, discover that unseen force? And what if, once you made this discovery, you became aware of a few simple actions you could take that would make dramatic improvements to your performance?"

A round of tug-o-war broke out inside me: Part of me bought in to what he was saying and was dying to hear what came next. And part of me was laughing at how it felt like I was on the set of "Field of Dreams 2.0."

"And if I build it will they come?" I said in an effort to keep the moment from getting too spooky.

"They're already here," he shot back with a chuckle that made the moment too spooky. "But let's call it a thing for now. So more accurately, 'it' is already here. Would you like to see it?"

"Sure."

It was yet another one of those times I committed early.

Here I was in the middle of a championship game talking to some guy I don't even know (or do I?) about some long dead European doctor and now I just agreed to do something that will "change my mind forever" and I don't even know what it is.

But it would have to wait until next inning. Waddle ended the inning by grounding out to third. I grabbed my glove and trotted out to

I felt a calm excitement as the ball popped into my glove during our arm-loosening infield throws. The man seemed to have warmed me up for something big. Yes, this was a championship game, but there was much more going on here.

It might have been a stretch at that moment to call it magical or mystical, but not for much longer.

Things were about to get pretty wild just outside that first base dugout.

The Energy of Baseball

After three mercifully quick outs, I was back at the fence.

"Alright, mister, what have you got in the bag for me?"

"Okay, ready to see it? Here you go," said the man reaching his hand up toward the top of the fence. I was about to see this world-changing device, or whatever it was.

I looked up and saw his hand over the top of the fence. I was instantly disappointed.

"Sunglasses? My mind is going to be changed by a pair of sunglasses?"

"Not just any sunglasses," the man said.

He was right: they were ugly sunglasses. They looked like a cross between Special Ops goggles and those goofy big sunglasses old people wear over their glasses. Make them hot pink instead of a military green and they'd be straight from some crazy music video.

I instinctively reached up and took them from his hand. With us both so close to the fence I could really feel the man's energy. He was essentially the same size as me. I tried to get a good look at his face through the screen but he was twisting to the side to reach higher and his arm blocked my view of his face.

"Got it," I said as I clasped the glasses. "Thanks," I said in a tone that silently added a sarcastic "I guess."

I hoped he didn't sense my disappointment.

"I know they aren't much to look at," he said, "but they're made to be looked through, not at."

"Oooh, I know," I said almost mockingly. "Are they super duper X-ray ugly glasses that enable me to see like Superman?"

"Actually, yes," he said, smacking down my attitude (which was really a cover for my nervousness).

I held the glasses in both hands as I checked them out. There was much more to them than those over-the-glasses shades. Much more.

They were heavy and felt solid. The lenses were dark and pretty thick. Clearly some electronics were involved, but nothing I really recognized.

"What's the E for?" I said, pointing to the letter molded on the sides of the glasses.

"I'm going to make you guess."

"May I try them on?" I asked.

"Of course," said the man.

I wasn't as nervous as I should have been.

Seeing Reality for the First Time

I turned to face the field. For some reason I closed my eyes as I slipped the glasses on with both hands. The glasses were heavy but pretty comfortable.

I opened my eyes and was taken aback by a rich pageant of colors and shapes. I knew I was seeing the field and the players, but not clearly. The players looked more like blobs. I could make out the shapes of the Rakeops players in their positions, and as I scanned side to side I saw Sammy Ginzburg, our hitter, at the plate.

But everything looked very strange. There was a kaleidoscope of colors and lines and grid-like geometric shapes.

"Cool," I said as I continued to adjust to the view. "This is like being in a video game. Very cool!"

"Yes," said the man, patiently waiting for me to orient myself.

"It's like those night vision goggles," I said. "It's clear enough to see what or who I'm looking at, but they have a glow about them. And instead of being black or gray in between people it's a beautiful blue."

"Yes, go on," said the man, "tell me what else you notice."

"I see several different colors. It's beautiful, really. Sort of like MRI glasses, I see different colors glowing out of different people and different things. The people are either blue or red. Different shades of blue or red. And they're different sizes, too. Why is that?"

"We'll discuss it all in a minute," said the man. "Just keep telling me what you notice. Take your time."

"What am I seeing?" I asked, "What do these glasses do?"

"You tell me," said the man, again deflecting my questions. "What do you think you're seeing?"

I took a few more moments to study. I'd adjusted enough to think clearly and review my observations.

For the most part, the colors were brilliant. Some players were brighter and bigger than others. Some were more blue, others more red.

There was a beautiful blue anywhere there wasn't some other color.

And everything was vibrating.

"Everything looks alive," I started. "Even the things that aren't. So I guess I'm seeing life. You were right about the X-ray vision, in a way, but this isn't just X-ray vision, it's more like one of those heat maps where you see the temperature of things."

"Good, good," said the man, "go on."

"And everything's buzzing, vibrating. Some things are vibrating fast, some slow. It's like everything is energized."

"Yes, so everything is... ," said the man, clearly knowing the answer.

"So everything is... ," I paused, clearly not knowing the answer.

"You just said it," prodded the man, with his first hint of impatience.

"Energized?" I said.

"Yes," said the man, "so everything is ..."

"Energy?"

"Yes," said the man with the authority and pride of a great teacher.

"Everything is energy."

"So I'm seeing energy. Like these glasses are microscopes or magnifying glasses that make me see energy?"

"You got it," he said. "That's what the 'E' stands for. The brand name is Energeticles."

"Cool. Very cool. Where can I get a pair?"

"You can't," said the man.

"What's up with the buzzing?" I said. "Even the non-living things have a vibration to them."

"You're seeing the Field," the man said.

"Yes," I said, "of course. But now there are all kinds of colors and lines on it.

"That's the Field. Not the baseball field; THE Field.

"What do you mean?"

"We call these 'Field Glasses.' They enable you to see The Field of energy we live in."

I stood silently to let it all sink in, trying to wrap my brain around it. It was like someone for the first time demonstrating to me that the world was round, not flat.

The man launched into lecture mode: "Albert Einstein was voted the number one biggest brain of the 1900s but no one pays attention to what he said."

"I know he said E = MC2," I said, hoping he wouldn't ask me what it means.

"Yes, but do you know what that means?"

"No."

"Ultimately it means everything is energy.
Einstein concluded that energy and
matter are one and the same thing,
and that we don't live in a universe with discrete,
separate objects with dead space between them.
Everything is connected, it's all part
of one big field, and it's all energy.

"So the ball field you are looking at, as well as the rest of the Universe, is one whole thing. And that one whole thing is energy."

"I'll bet this will make the pitchers happy," I said.

"Why's that?"

"No one can hit their pitches out of this field."

"Good one," smiled the man.

My mind was still whirling: "Do these glasses add color and stuff to graphically represent the energy on the field?"

"No," said the man, "these glasses enable you to see things the way they actually are. Everything is energy. That's all there is in the whole universe, including Matson Field."

I grunted a response that meant both "cool" and "I don't really get it."

"Remember we said that the big breakthroughs aren't about inventing something new, they're about seeing things more like they actually are. Remember Dr. Semmelweis?"

"Sure, the germ guy."

"Did he invent germs?"

"No."

"No, germs have been around longer than people have. Millions of people had no doubt died from germs before we even knew they existed. Semmelweis just figured out there was something going on he couldn't see profoundly affecting his patients' health."

"So these are like microscope glasses, enabling me to see what's really there but my naked eyes can't see."

"Exactly!" said the man.

"This is really cool," I said, starting to compare the energies of the different players and paying closer attention to how the energy was flowing and moving in addition to vibrating. "But so what? It's not like we just discovered germs and we need to wash our hands. How is this a game changer? How do I use this info to dominate on the field?"

"Good question," said the man, ***"knowledge is useless without action.*** We'll be doing nothing short of re-defining the game of baseball for you in just a few minutes. I'll give you a new game to play on this newly discovered field."

"Cool."

"But first let's dig deeper and start making some observations about what you see. Once we better understand what's going on it's easier to understand what you need to do to play better.

"Because, like Semmelweis and the germs, when you understand what's really going on, what's really affecting how the game goes and how your performance goes, you'll see some simple things you can do to dramatically improve your performance."

"Cool," I said, still marveling at the view. Then I added with a nervous laugh, "Are you going to make me wash my hands before each at-bat?"

"Not exactly, but you will want to do some tapping."

Picking Up Good Vibrations

When the man mentioned "tapping," I had no idea what he was talking about. But then again, considering I was looking through this pair of glasses seeing energy, I was eager to take in all he had to tell me.

"The most important thing I want you to pay attention to right now," the man said, "is the frequency of the vibrations of the different players.

Everything is vibrating because everything is energy, and energy vibrates.

It's all just vibrating so fast, even the 'slow' vibrations, that even things look solid. It's like an electric fan: when it's turned off you can see right through it, see the different fins of it. But when it's spinning it looks like a solid."

"Got it," I said.

"You yourself are actually just like that spinning fan. You aren't really solid like you think," said the man.

"Yes, I know, I got a little soft in the belly this summer."

"No," said the man, not sure if I was kidding or not. "I mean you're made up of about 50 trillion cells and they're not solid. You're literally vibrating right now. If you could stop the vibrating we could see right through you."

"Like a stopped fan," I said, my mind spinning like an electric fan.

"Like a stopped fan. Now tell me what you notice about the vibrations of different players you see. What do you notice right away?"

"That they're vibrating at different speeds, like different frequencies. Some are faster, like Kamin's, and some are slower... like...," I scanned the field, "like their second baseman. He looks awful. What's up with him?"

"Very good," said the man. "Not hard to notice the extremes. Most players are in sort of a middle range. Let's see what we can learn by looking at the extremes, like we did with your ABCs. You're a college boy, so let me give you a classic college essay question: Compare and contrast the energies of their pitcher, Kamin, with their second baseman."

"Well," I began, "it's pretty obvious that vibrating at a higher frequency is better."

"I agree, and tell me why you say that."

"First, I already knew Kamin is pitching great and I've seen their second baseman struggle both on defense and at the plate. But even without knowing how they're playing, the glow around Kamin is obviously bigger, it makes him look and feel bigger. I know when I'm confident I feel bigger."

"Yes," said the man, "like you Act Big?"

"For sure," I said, "bigger is better, at least when it comes to how I feel on a baseball field."

"Think back to your Detroit Lakes game," said the man, "did you have a sense your energy was big and expanding, or small and contracting?"

"Big and expanding, for sure."

"And when you're playing badly, like their second baseman?"

"Contracting, big time. I feel like everything is closing in on me. I feel...., well, I feel like that second baseman looks!"

"Yes, so remember that distinction between expanding and contracting, big and small. You'll play better and have more fun when your energy is expanding. When you're thinking negatively your energy contracts. That's playing small. Remember, they call poor performances under pressure 'choking.' Everything tightens around you and it makes it hard to breathe. And go on. What else do you notice?"

"The energy blob around Kamin is a nice strong blue, while the second baseman is red. Is that just the difference between positive and negative energy?"

"Yes, the high frequency, positive energy is blue, and the negative red. What else?"

"Kamin's energy blob is flowing freely. Energy is flowing and moving through him way better than the second baseman, who looks pretty blocked up. Not much flow in and out."

"Right on. When you're vibrating at a high frequency, energy is flowing through you freely. Athletes sometimes call a peak state of performance being in 'flow' because that's what it feels like. You're just seeing that it's literal. Energy is actually flowing through them freely."

I nodded my head. With these glasses the differences in the energy of playing great versus playing poorly were perfectly clear. Actually, I wasn't seeing anything I hadn't suspected before. At least everything I was now seeing resonated as true to what I'd felt a million times but I never could have articulated it before.

"Poor performance," the man continued, "and, as we'll see shortly, feeling bad, results from blocked energy flow, or you could say, a disruption in your energy flow. You feel these blocks as negative emotions."

"How do you unblock yourself?" I asked.

"We'll get there, 21, but we're still discovering the nature of the universe, we'll get to improvement shortly."

"Okay. Well, I can also see that Kamin's energy seems more focused. It's all clearly directed at the plate, especially once he steps on the rubber. He's clear, focused, like he's on a mission."

"Yes," said the man, "and the second baseman?"

"Scattered. His energy doesn't seem organized like Kamin's. Sort of all over the place. But, actually, mostly his energy, like his focus, is on himself. Whereas Kamin's energy is going out toward the plate."

"Yes, that's the last distinction I wanted you to get about player's energy: the degree to which it's focused. In particular, *to perform well, you need all your energy focused on your target. You need to focus your energy on what you want. That's what Kamin is doing. The second baseman's focusing his energy on what he doesn't want. No mystery which focus gives you your best chance to play well, eh?*"

"Nope."

"In your psych classes they call it a self-fulfilling prophesy. That second baseman is thinking, 'Don't hit it to me, I'll boot it or throw it away, or I'll get a bad hop' and of course..."

"He'll boot it," I said, taking my turn to finish the man's thought.

After a pause I added: "I guess with all that anxiety he's in that famous life question Shakespeare asked."

"Which one's that?" said the man.

"2B or not 2B?"

"Ugh," groaned the man.

"Couldn't pass it up," I said, "after your 'who's on first?' line."

"Try harder next time," said the man.

"Will do."

"To play your best you need your energy to be vibrating at a high frequency, positive, expanding, flowing, and focused. And of course all those things go together. If you have one you're almost assured of having the others."

"That keeps it simple," I said.

"That's right," the man said, "Keepin' it simple."

The Energy of Excellence

As I continued to look through the man's magical glasses, I started to make an observation about Kamin.

"You know," I said, "it's cool to see this because before I had these glasses on, I think I could feel what I'm now seeing. Kamin has great energy on the mound. He's intimidating because he has, I don't know, sort of an aura around him."

"Go on," said the man.

"It's just harder to feel comfortable with him on the mound. Other pitchers might have as good of stuff, but Kamin just messes with our confidence somehow. Now I can see what I've been feeling. In fact, I feel like I might be able to sense people's energy, at least in the extreme cases. Not like Darth Vader feeling a disruption in the Force, but kind of."

"Absolutely," said the man. "And now that you've actually seen what's there you'll be much more sensitive to it. You and everyone else are picking all this up all the time, you usually just aren't aware of it. You sense and assess someone's energy the instant you meet them. You just don't think in energy terms, until now. Now it will be hard to turn it off."

"That's pretty freaky."

"Right on," the man praised.

"Ok, review time," he added. "You noticed five qualities of energy. Can you remember what they are and how they differ between playing big and playing small?"

Playing Big Energy	*Playing Small Energy*
Positive	Negative
Expanding	Contracting
High Frequency/Light	Low Frequency/Heavy
Flowing Freely	Blocked
Focused	Fractured

"When you're big, playing well, feeling good," I began, "your energy is positive, expanding, vibrating at a high frequency, flowing freely, and focused."

"Yes," said the man, "and you feel light."

"And when you're playing poorly and feeling bad," I reported, "your energy is negative, contracting. It's vibrating slowly so it's a low frequency. It's blocked somewhere, by something, probably an emotion, and your focus is fractured – it's divided between multiple things."

"Yes," the man agreed, "it's split or focused on the wrong thing at that moment.

It's actually a good idea to check in on your own energy between pitches or innings, but when it's time to perform, your focus needs to go out onto whatever the critical variable at the moment is: the ball if you're hitting or playing defense, and the target if you're pitching.

"Got it," I said. "But that already seems like a lot to remember."

"Sure," said the man, "but you really only have to remember one of them. They all go together. *You basically can just ask yourself whether you like the way you're feeling.* Just that simple question puts you on the right track. Then you can go through each of these finer distinctions to get more clarity for yourself."

"So I'd say, 'Do I feel like I'm big and expanding right now or small and contracting?'"

"Exactly," said the man. "Or, 'do I feel free or blocked? Focused or Fractured?' 'Light or heavy?' and so on."

"So what do I do if I don't like the way I feel?" I asked. "How do you get the good vibes going? How do you release your blocks? There are so many bad things that happen to you in baseball it's hard to keep on that playing well side."

"First," said the man, clearly enjoying my growing energy, "just becoming aware of your energy will usually trigger an improvement. Even if you feel pretty good, checking in on yourself and really noticing what you're feeling will naturally

cause you to make an upgrade to how you're feeling without your even trying to do something different."

"So I need to be more aware of my feelings," I groaned, "just what a guy wants to hear."

"You'll get over it. Your feelings are a built in device that will guide you toward your best performance, but most players try their best to ignore their feelings. They're really your best friend, guide, and teacher."

I understood what he meant, but it felt like a stretch to me.

"But there's a lot more you can do. I'll give you things soon you can do that will instantly amp you up, and I'll give you exercises that that build your energy over time, through repetitions, like the way you build a muscle in the gym."

We paused to watch Kamin throw another strike.

"But you aren't ready for that, young Padawan," the man continued. "The number one point I wanted you to get about the universe is that everything is energy. And everything has a vibration to it that ranges from high to low. High frequency is positive, flowing, expanding and focused. Low frequency vibrations are negative, blocked, contracting and scattered.

"Got it," I said, "everything is energy and everything is vibrating."

"Now you're ready for the second point. It's the law that determines what happens in baseball."

"The law that if I follow it I'll become a great player?"

"You have no choice about this law. You're following it now and you've always followed it, so has everyone else. You can't opt out of this law any more than you can opt out of the law of gravity. It's just that you don't know it. And because you don't know it you suffer way more than you have to and you play much below the level you could."

"Okay, okay, what is it?" I asked.

Questions to Consider for Part 4

1. What did you learn from the story of Dr. Semmelweiss?

2. What Field are you REALLY playing on? ("21" had to see this fact to believe it)

3. What are the 5 differences in energy between playing big and playing small?

4. What is the built-in device you already have that will guide you to high-level performance (but you're probably trying to ignore it)

Part 5:

"The Hidden Law that Determines Your Success in Baseball (and Life)"

You're about to discover...

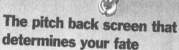

- The pitch back screen that determines your fate

- The one term that captures the key to success

- Why it matters that your unconscious brain controls 90% or more of what you do

- The surprisingly simple recipe for getting whatever you want

- How to get to the "Bigs" every day (and why you need to)

- What to focus on to attract success like a super-magnet

Find out at:

PlayBigBaseball.com

The Law that Governs Baseball

The man could sense my impatience, but, as with most everything so far, he wanted to make me come to my own answer.

"Remember our guiding principle is simplicity," he said.

"Simple wins," I said proudly.

"This law takes everything we've talked about so far and boils it down into one idea. In fact, it takes everything about baseball and boils it down into one idea. This law is acting on everyone out here all the time, whether they're playing baseball or not. Understanding this law is the key to..."

"Well," I said impatiently, "what is it?"

"The law is called the Law of Attraction."

The Law of Attraction? Once again the man had built a bunch of drama about something and once again it disappointed me. But the ugly sunglasses had turned out to be very cool, so I hoped the Law of Attraction was more than met the eye as well.

"The Law of Attraction says 'that which is like itself is drawn.' A more familiar way of saying it is birds of a feather flock together,' or 'like attracts like.'"

"Okay," I said, obviously not yet impressed.

"Thanks to those glasses you see it happening out there right now," he said. "Look at the energy coming in to Kamin versus the energy coming in to the second baseman."

"Kamin's got a lot of the good blue stuff coming in, and the other guy only red negative stuff."

"Right. And can you see that they are both bringing in what they are giving off?

"Yes."

"And you can see the results they're producing. Those results stem from their vibrations."

"Hmm," I uttered, not committing to buying the idea or rejecting it.

"Imagine yourself as a giant broadcasting and receiving station. You're broadcasting your thoughts and emotions out into that Field. Imagine that every thought you have is sent out into the giant energy field. That's your vibration, you're always broadcasting your vibration, and it goes rippling out through the energy field."

"Okay."

"That energy bounces off everything else out there and comes right back at you in some physical way. The quality of what comes back to you is a match for what you sent out there in the first place.

"You get back what you give out to The Field in terms of your vibration, your energy.

"The universe sends you results, people and experiences that are a vibrational match for what you are sending out."

Remember those 'pitch-back' screens you probably used as a kid, where you could throw the ball into the net and it'd come back to you?"

"Sure, those things are awesome."

"That's just the way the universe works: Whatever you throw out at it comes shooting back at you. With the pitch back if you throw the ball hard it comes back hard; if you throw it soft it comes back soft. With the universe if you send out good vibes you get good news back, and if you send out bad vibes you get bad news back. Can't get much simpler than that."

"Huhm," I said (a combination of a thoughtful hmmm and an I'm-not-so-sure huh?).

"You get back what you give off," I said, considering the idea.

"You got it," the man said. "And you can take this literally, meaning what I'm saying about sending a vibration 'out to The Field' is all actually true as I'm describing it, or figuratively, meaning this is one way of thinking about what's happening. I don't care which way you go, but I do want you to get that your performance and everything else in your life is going to be tons better the higher vibe you're giving off."

The universe is like a giant pitch back screen: You get back what you send out. Send out good vibes and you get back good news...

... send out bad vibes and you get back bad news.

"Well," I said, "it's hard not to take it literally when I can see it happening live through these funky glasses."

"All you have to remember is the term *vibrational match*."

"Vibrational match?" I said, requesting clarification.

"Yes. You attract things into your experience that are a vibrational match to you. During your first AB today you were a vibrational match for bad hitting. Your vibe attracted a bad AB. Kamin is a vibrational match for high-level pitching right now, and that's what he's getting."

"I see."

"We'll get to this in depth in a moment, but *the key to getting anything you want is you must first become a vibrational match for it*. You must vibrate at a frequency that will attract or allow that result to happen. The game is to raise your vibration to a level that matches what you want before you get what you want."

"I think I get that," I said.

"Let's look at some more examples. Do you have a special circumstance where you have trouble performing?"

"That's kind of a personal question, sir," I said with a wry smile.

"I mean on the field. Is there a situation that bugs you, where you consistently can't perform well?"

"Well," I said slowly, thinking. "I sometimes help out with an Under 14 team by throwing batting practice for them and there's one kid I have a hard time throwing strikes to."

"Let me guess," said the man, shifting for the first time into a sarcastic tone, "and this will take all my psychic powers. I'm going to say that out of that whole team he's the one guy you'd also pick as the guy who gets the most upset about bad BP" [batting practice pitching].

"ABSOLUTELY!" I declared. "The guy's a real jerk about it. I feel like he's getting in the cage saying 'you better throw well' and I can feel myself tense up. I tell myself 'Okay, nice and easy; throw strikes to this guy.' Then I throw one or two bad pitches, he gets mad, and I fall apart. Then I'll pump strikes to the very next guy."

"That's the Law of Attraction in action for both of you," said the man. "He actually attracts bad BP by focusing on bad BP.

What we focus on expands and we get more of.

"So when he gets in the cage with 'don't screw up my BP' vibes he's attracting bad BP. You could say his negative energy about BP is projected out to you and interrupts your energy flow. But the coaching for him is to focus on what he wants. He's focused on what he doesn't want – even though he wouldn't admit it and consciously he probably has no idea he's doing it – so he gets what he doesn't want."

"Yes, he certainly gets my worst BP," I said.

"Now, you can't control him, of course, so your lesson is that you're a big boy and responsible for your own energy.

You aren't a helpless victim here."

I nodded.

"Focus is a key element to your vibe. What you focus on you vibrate so what you focus on you attract. When your focus is 'I better throw well to this guy or he'll get mad,' it's fear talking. You're afraid of his reaction to you.

An untrained person typically focuses on what he fears… and so he attracts it.

"Your fear makes you contract and lose your freedom. Your muscles tighten and you get distracted easily or focus on the wrong things. You need to develop your ability to manage your energy, upgrade your beliefs, and focus your focus. Playing big is a trained skill."

"I'd like to be able to overcome his being angry and throw well anyway," I said. "I do sometimes, but usually I feel like such a wimp that I can't get over it."

"The Force is strong with one who has anger," the man said in a bad Yoda voice. "Train you must, strengthen you will."

"Actually", I then added, "now that I think about it there's also a Little League kid I was throwing to the other day who was afraid of the ball. He kept backing out just as I was releasing the ball. And of all the kids I threw to that day he's…"

"The only one you hit," the man jumped in.

"The only one I hit," I said redundantly.

"Exactly. His energy on 'don't get hit' attracted his getting hit, mixed with your energy on 'don't hit this kid' make a dangerous HBP [hit by pitch] cocktail. It doesn't mean you'll for sure hit him, but it certainly puts that card in the deck. Remember, what you think about and how you feel determines your vibration, and that determines what you attract. Birds of a feather flock together, so your thoughts and your results are drawn together."

"So 'vibes of a feather flock together?'" I said.

"Excellent," the man said, "I'm going to steal that one."

"No charge."

"Remember one of the first things I told you was that you were asking for more bad hitting?"

"Of course. It seemed ridiculous."

"That's the Law of Attraction. You were vibrating at a very low frequency – frustration, anger, even powerlessness – and so you were in effect telling The Field you wanted more bad hitting.

"So what you're vibing you're asking for?"

"Yes. Your thoughts and emotions are like requests going out to the universe, to The Field of energy we're surrounded by, that we're a part of."

"But it's not like I control my feelings."

"But it is like you can," the man shot back. "With practice you can get very good at it. We'll get to that later, but I really want to hammer this Law of Attraction. It's very simple, but its effects are profound."

"I hear you," I said. "But that's easier said than done isn't it? How do you get good at controlling your thoughts and feelings?"

"We're almost ready for that," said the man.

Just then it was time to play defense again.

"I'll take those glasses back," said the man.

"Oh, ya," I said, passing them back over the fence. "Thanks."

"You're welcome. Just remember: Everything is energy, so energy is everything."

"Got it." I grabbed my glove and headed back out, wondering what I was attracting now.

The Core of Success Revealed

As was the case for two games now, I couldn't get the man's words out of my head while I was in the field. So, as soon as I got back to the fence after the inning, I tried to poke holes in this Law of Attraction.

"But," I said, my mind comparing what the man was saying to my own experience, "you make it sound like anything I think about will magically appear. I imagined each hitter that inning hitting me a ground ball and none of them did."

"I understand that's what you heard me say, but that's not what I actually said or mean. It isn't immediate. You're not some genie that makes things appear and disappear instantly. It's not like you think a good thought and some-

thing good immediately happens. You can't think about a person and have him or her show up instantly."

"If you could there'd be a lot of good-looking girls in our dugout right now," I quipped.

"Exactly," laughed the man.

"A thought sets things in motion. It starts the process of bringing whatever you're thinking about, whatever you're vibrating, toward you. In order for it to show up, in other words, in order for you to attract it, you have to first maintain your focus on it over time. A thought plants a seed. Seeds grow into plants, right?"

"Yes."

"But that seed needs time and the proper care to come to fruition. You need to focus and cultivate your thoughts before they manifest."

"I see."

"That's why all the success teachers talk about the importance of holding your focus on what you want. Read your goals each night before bed, they'll say, and read them again each morning when you wake up. Do this over and over for days until it becomes part of you. Until it's embedded into your cells that it's what you want, and you know deep down you deserve to have it. So while every thought you have makes a difference in your vibration, one thought

held for just a few moments isn't going to change your world much. *It takes some farming before you harvest.*"

"That makes sense," I said.

"If it helps, think of it as your having a 'surface vibration' and a 'core vibration.'"

"Okay."

"While your surface vibration changes with your thoughts, much the way we changed your vibration going through the ABCs a couple of innings ago, the major circumstances in your life stem from your core vibration, which would be more commonly called your core beliefs.

"These core beliefs make up your identity, your self-image, who you believe yourself to be.

Nothing is more important to your baseball success and your enjoyment of life than your core beliefs.

You simply do not outperform your core beliefs. You play only at a level you believe you can play."

"Ah, yeah," I said.

"If you do have a streak where you play really great for a while, better than in your cells you believe you should play, you'll find a way to sabotage it. And pretty soon you're right back in your comfort zone, right where you believe you belong."

"Been there," I said.

"Your conscious mind says it wants to play better," the man rolled on, "but our conscious minds are no match for our unconscious minds. Our unconscious minds, our core beliefs, run the show. As you might guess, *the real key to playing big and finding out how good you can be in baseball or anything else is having big beliefs."*

"Bigger is better."

"You might tell yourself, 'I can hit this guy.' You might even repeat it over and over. But that's a surface thought. You definitely want your surface thoughts headed in the right direction. I'm talking about a belief. A belief is a thought you keep thinking. You've thought it many times and it's literally embedded in the cells of your body. A belief isn't just something you have in your head. It's in every part of you."

I shook my head as Kamin got another out. *Would we ever score off this guy?* At least the Rakeops hadn't scored against us yet.

"So it's not as easy and fast to change it as it is to change your immediate state. We changed how you felt in the moment with your ABCs and that's hugely important. Generating confidence and focus like that is the absolute best thing you can do come game time.

"But the real determinant of how well you play and what happens to you over the course of a season are your core beliefs, which make your core vibration. Your core vibration is what is broadcast out into the Field, and has been for a

much longer time than your surface thoughts. The seeds of your core beliefs have had years to grow."

"How do I change my core vibration and beliefs?" I asked.

"A belief is a thought you keep thinking, so one way is just to do your ABCs over and over. That way you condition yourself to make being confident your habit Repetition of your ABCs gradually changes your beliefs at the unconscious, cellular level. I've got an incredibly powerful way to improve your core beliefs. I'll teach it to you if we have time later."

I nodded. This was a lot to take in. We obviously were going through some "complexity."

"Just like it takes some time to build up muscles," the man said, "it takes some time to change your core beliefs."

"Sounds like that would be a good thing to focus on," I said.

"It's the most important thing to focus on.

There's nothing more helpful to your baseball career and the rest of your life than raise your core vibration.

And don't get hung up on surface vs. core vibration. Just focus on feeling good."

"Nice simplification," I said.

"Thank you. And get this: if you feel frustrated about your hitting, hard work is not going to improve it. Not while you're frustrated. That would violate the Law of Attraction. Your low vibration thinking will attract low vibration results no matter how many balls you whack off a tee. If you're angry because your teammates aren't pulling their weight the way you think they should, no angry speech from you will change them. That would violate the law of attraction.

"The Law of Attraction simply and accurately gives you back, in a wide variety of ways, what you're broadcasting out. What you get is a vibrational match for your current vibration.

"So if you want conditions around you to change, change your feeling to the way you'd feel if they already changed."

"Sounds like you want me to play 'make believe.'"

"You must make believe before you can make real, 21. Can I promise you it will change instantly? No. But I can promise you nothing will change until you do. And as you begin to line up as a vibrational match for what you want, the seed for it has been planted and the thing you want is on its way to you."

"So we're back to why you were saying I was asking for more bad hitting," I said. "You're saying my anger and frustration and negative thinking were sending out vibes that were like a request for more bad hitting. My thoughts and feelings are a request for more of what I am thinking and feeling."

"You got it," said the man.

How to Get What You Want

I was completely engrossed in the conversation. I knew there was a game going on, but it almost didn't seem to matter. I could feel my own energy building from the coaching I was getting and sensed it could help us win this game.

"Now we've covered the two key ideas I wanted to about the universe: one, that everything is energy, and two, that the Law of Attraction is always in play bringing together things that are a vibrational match for each other.

"Do you remember the second major big idea besides the universe I said we'd address?"

"Me. You said we'd look at the nature of me. My favorite topic."

"Yes. And since you're part of the universe, we've already covered two important things about you."

"Well, I'm something, so I must be made of energy."

"Correct. You're energy and thus you have a vibration. You're a vibrational being."

"Cool."

"And what else do you now know about yourself?"

"I guess that the Law of Attraction is always in play for me."

"Meaning...."

"I get back what I broadcast out. I'm attracting things, experiences, results, that are a vibrational match for what I'm feeling. The universe is like a giant pitch-back screen."

"Very nice. If you just remember that idea of 'vibrational match' you're in good shape. It pretty much e plains everything. Let me show you: draw a line in the dirt in front of you running up and down, or north and south. This line represents a continuum of vibrational frequencies. At the top is high frequency, or high vibration, and at the bottom is low frequency and low vibration. During every moment of every day, you're somewhere on that continuum."

"But how do I know where? How do I know what I'm vibrating?"

"Great question. Two answers: First, by the results you're getting. Since you attract what you vibrate you can simply look around you and see how things are going and know they're a mirror of your vibration.

Two Ways to Know What You're Vibrating

1. **The results you're getting.**
2. **How you feel.**

"And second, how you feel. Your feelings correspond to your vibration. So at the top of our north-south line, at the high frequency level, you have freedom, joy, passion, love of the game. When you're vibrating at the level of freedom, where you play totally free of fears and distractions and freely swing the bat or throw the ball with total trust, you attract good things. You're playing big."

"That's confidence."

"Yes, and I say even a level above confidence. Playing with confidence is one thing, but playing with freedom is even a level higher."

"I think I get that," I said.

"On the other end of the scale is fear and powerlessness. By powerlessness I mean you feel like giving up because nothing you do seems to make any difference.

"Been there."

"Indeed," said the man. "That's a low-end vibe. No fun."

"I'll say."

"So the answer to your question about how do you know what you're vibrating is what?"

"What results I'm getting for one…"

"Yes."

"And how I'm feeling for two."

"Right on," said the man. "Think of your feelings as your built in Global Positioning System, your GPS Your feelings tell you where you are on this north-south continuum. I like to call it my Greatness Positioning System since it

tells me where I am in relation to being great. There are an infinite number of places you can be on this continuum, but let's pick out five of them just to keep it simple."

"Okay."

"At the top as I said is freedom, joy, love of the game, all those we'll count as one. And then below that we'll call confidence. In the middle we'll call it 'trying,' 'efforting,' or 'okay.' You aren't really in a good place, but you aren't in bad shape either. This middle spot is grinding it out. You're doing fine, but it takes effort, you're working it."

"If you wanted it really simple we could just say love at the top, which means free and fun, like when you were a kid playing WIFFLE ball or in your DL game.

And fear at the bottom.
Fear is all the negative side of the different aspects of energy we discussed: negative, constricting, blocked, and a scattered focus."

"I'm there a lot, I think."

"Sure. Most players are. Below that, now we're south of the midpoint, we'll put frustration and anger. Frustration would be higher than anger, but to keep it simple we group them together."

"I think we've both seen me there," I said.

"And at the bottom as I said is fear and powerlessness."

"My good friends," I said.

"I know that bottom feeling."

"Yes. And I like to put things on a zero to 10 scale. So you can put a zero down at the bottom with fear and powerlessness, move up to a two and four or so with anger then fear. Then five is feeling okay, six would be hope, eight confidence, and 10 is freedom, joy, love and fun."

"So I'd say when we met yesterday I was about a 1 or 0," I said, pointing to the lower end of the vertical line in the dirt. "And I've climbed pretty steadily since. The ABC's moved me up pretty close to confidence. I felt pretty good this last AB, but certainly not like I did for the DL game which would be up here at the top."

"I agree 100 percent."

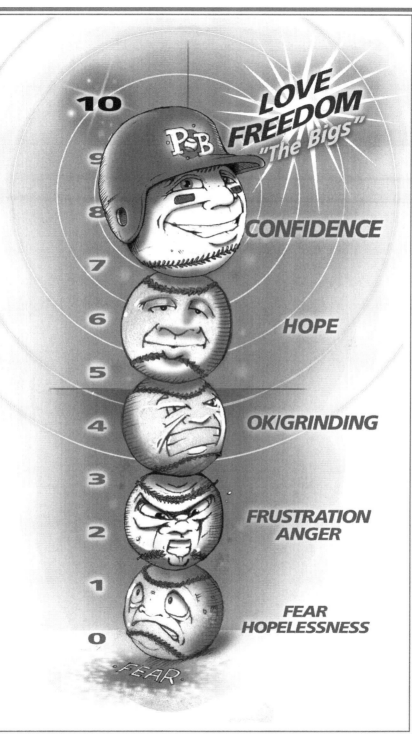

How to Get to the Bigs

"When you're at the top of that continuum, say an eight or better you feel great," said the man. "Your vibration is big, your energy is big, you feel big, your energy flow is big, your confidence is big, you act big, you breathe big and you commit big. So I call it The Bigs."

"You mean like the big leagues?"

"Yes, except that *The Bigs as I mean it is a feeling, not a place.* Imagine you're now a star player in the actual big leagues, how would that feel?"

"Awesome."

"Yes, and while you can't magically put yourself in the major leagues, you can generate major-league good vibes by creative, smart use of your focus."

I nodded.

"We've already covered the key elements of playing in The Bigs, your ABCs."

"Act Big, Breathe Big, and Commit Big," I said quickly, the words rolling off my tongue as if I'd been saying them since I first learned to speak.

"Yes," said the man enthusiastically, "those are the basics of how to get to The Bigs."

"So doing my ABCs gets me to The Bigs..."

"They at least get you heading north on our continuum. They won't automatically put you there, of course. That depends on what vibration level you're starting out at and how much you've practiced raising your vibe."

"I see."

"Just think of The Bigs as feeling really great. When you feel really great you're free. Free of fear, doubt, anxiousness, frustration and concern over what other people think about you. You're free to play like you did when you were a little kid, and free to just pour your talent out onto the field."

The idea was starting to make sense – *The Bigs is a feeling, not a place.*

"The Bigs includes feeling gratitude, happiness, contentment. You're very present (as in not distracted), peaceful, really enjoying the moment you're living right now. You might be pumped up or you might be calm, but you feel great."

"Sounds good to me," I said. "I've had moments of that, I guess, but not too often."

"That's about to change," said the man. "If you want. The key step is making feeling great your goal."

"Is The Bigs the same as the zone?"

"No. The zone, as people talk about it, is where everything seems like it's in slow motion, like you're in total control and everything is easy. That's part of The Bigs, but The Bigs is something bigger, broader.

"The zone is usually thought of as something you go into during performance, and it's short-lived. You can be in The Bigs any time, in fact, with practice, almost all the time. When you were in that game in Detroit Lakes you were in The Bigs, and probably in the zone too. But don't get hung up on being too specific about it. *Worrying about whether you're in the zone or The Bigs takes you right out of both of them!*"

"Keepin' it simple," I said.

"Imagine being in The Bigs," said the man, "feeling really great."

"Okay," I said, imagining myself happy as a clam.

"Do things seem easier or harder?"

"Much easier. When I'm feeling great I can just do things with very little effort, whether it's baseball or school or talking to girls. Everything is easier when I feel great."

"That's because you are being fully you."

"Fully me?"

"Yes, when you're in The Bigs it isn't that you've added things on to you. You haven't added confidence and enthusiasm. It's actually that you've dropped your emotional baggage. You aren't loaded down by any negative emotions or distracting thoughts about what other people are thinking about you. You're just...you."

I nodded.

"It's like the difference between a hot, high humidity day and a pleasant, zero humidity day. With high humidity, moving is work, like you're fighting your way through a big vat of honey. With no humidity you move freely, effortlessly. The difference isn't you; it's the environment you're in. In lower level vibrations you have to fight through heavy, negative energy. The Bigs is that zero humidity, zero honey environment."

"Sweet," I joked. I think the man got it, but he didn't bother acknowledging it.

"That 'DL You,'" he rolled on, "'The Bigs' you, isn't some strange fluke where you played better than you can play, where you felt better than you can feel, that you believed more that you can believe. It's just the opposite, 21, that is the **REAL YOU**. That is who you are."

"The answer to 'Who's on First?'"

"Yes!" laughed the man. "The rest of the time you're weighed down or distracted. You are pulled away from the real you by your thoughts about yourself and your thoughts about the actions of others and your thoughts about what happens in a game."

I nodded. I understood what he was saying, but I felt like my learning tank was almost full.

"Now you know when you feel off or when you feel bad or when you don't feel as good as you'd like it's because you're not in alignment with Big You."

"Never thought of it that way. But I guess that makes sense."

"That's the irony: People stress and strain thinking that if they get this or that it will make them happy, when real happiness – and better performance — actually comes from letting go."

"But I can't just smile my way to the real Big Leagues. I can't just be happy and think I'll be all-conference next season."

"You'd do much better than you think," laughed the man. "But you absolutely do need to practice and train your technique and your physical conditioning. You need to do your part and take the actions that are aligned with what you want. And – and this is HUGE –your practicing and training and playing will be much more effective if you do them in The Bigs, instead of thinking that doing them will get you there."

That one took a few moments to sink in. *Feel great and then practice while feeling great, instead of thinking that practicing will make me feel great.*

"I guess," I concluded, "since I do everything better when I feel good I'd practice better if I got myself to feel good first."

"Right on," said the man. "Do you think you'd practice more effectively, make adjustments to your swing and throw better, when you're practicing in a vat of honey or in zero humidity?"

"Got it," I said. "So get to The Bigs, or at least as close as I can, before I practice."

"That's huge. You'll acquire skills so much faster than if you're fighting through negative energy *and* trying to in-grain a new habit. That's why smart coaches don't create an environment of fear. They create a challenging environment, for sure, but one that frees players to play with passion instead of chaining them with fear.

"I'm sure you've heard of legendary basketball coach John Wooden, who was voted Coach of the Century. Many of his players used to say that their practices were so intense that the games became easy and fun."

"High vibe."

"High vibe. *But don't think your vibe is your coach's responsibility. It's yours. As soon as you blame someone else for your vibe you give away your power. You give away your most precious asset: your free will.*"

"Darn, I was hoping I could blame my slump on somebody."

"Sorry. You don't want to give away your power. If you're innocent, you're impotent."

"Ouch."

"Make The Bigs your guide. It's a feeling place where you have the most fun and where you play your best. The more you're in there the better you'll play. Before you take any action, be it in practice or a game, align yourself as best you can with The Bigs."

Feel good to perform,
don't perform to feel good."

"Mentally prepare myself," I said.

"Yes. *All great players are great preparers.* Plus, the more you're in The Bigs the more enjoyment you experience and the more you expand, meaning the more you become capable of in all areas of your life. So the two main reasons you play baseball, enjoyment and expansion, get met best when you are in The Bigs."

"Cool."

"To wrap this up, think of the Bigs as a guide. Like the North Star. Sailors and others use the North Star to navigate at night. If they know where north is they can get their bearings and head the direction they want to go. The nice thing is you always want to go north. So you just need to get a good idea of what feeling great feels like – and I think you already do – and head toward it all day every day."

"All day, every day?"

"Yes.

No matter what you're doing you want to head north, toward The Bigs. Remember, The Bigs is feeling great. When would you not want to feel great?"

"Well, never, but that's pretty unrealistic. No one feels great all the time, do they?"

"No," said the man. "But some feel great a lot more than others. Anyone can be there much more often if they focus on it and practice it. And since you play your best when you feel great, and feeling great just feels great, I say it makes sense to make feeling great a top priority. Actually, the top priority."

"It's funny how that makes sense on the one hand and seems sort of funny on the other."

"I know. It seems obvious to make feeling great a priority, but it also is a bit radical, too. Washing your hands before surgery seemed simple and obvious to Semmelweis, but it was radical at the time. But we don't have all day to talk about it and we're not done talking about you and how you are designed. There's another key element I need to tell you about."

"This is great," I said. "Why didn't you just tell me about all this from the beginning?"

"If I had opened with terms like 'vibrational match' and the Law of Attraction do you think we'd be talking right now?"

"Good point."

The Power of Focus

The man continued: "One other element is so crucial to your vibration and performance I put it on a separate but related line in our diagram. Draw a horizontal line through the dirt that cuts the vibe line in half."

I did so with the end of my bat, creating a big plus sign diagram.

"That line represents focus. On the far left is poor focus or scattered focus, and on the far right is total focus. In particular, when you're on the far right of this diagram you're focused on what you want."

"I certainly play better when I'm focused," I said.

"Absolutely. *Focus might be the single most important element of athletic performance.* It certainly makes up a big percentage of your vibration. As you get more focused on your target, on what you want, you move to the right on this diagram. And as you do that your vibration will always move toward The Bigs. So no matter how you feel, no matter what your vibe is, focusing on your target will help you."

"Got it," I said.

"Focus means to focus your energy. When you're putting your attention on something in the past you're focusing energy on that. When you're imagining about something in the future you're focusing energy on that. And when you're putting your attention on the present moment you're focusing energy on that.

"Whatever you focus your energy on – whether it be something in the past, future or present – becomes your vibration for that moment. When you spend more and more time focusing on something that becomes more and more your dominant vibration level. In other words: Energy flow makes things grow."

"Good one!" I said.

"Thank you. Came up with that one myself."

I repeated it: "Energy flow makes things grow."

"Your body is designed to hit targets and reach goals," the man rolled on, "this is how we survive. For example, your mind says 'find food, I'm hungry' and you go find food. Think of it this way: Performance follows focus.

"Our focus is like reins on a trained horse. If the reins are pulled right, the horse goes right. If the reins are pulled left, he goes left. If you're riding a bike straight ahead but turn to the right to check out an attractive view…"

"That's happened to me," I smiled.

"Then you know you won't be going straight any more. You'll veer to the right. You might *intend* to stay straight, but when your eyes and focus go right, your body goes right."

"My performance followed my focus," I summarized.

"Yes, so to be successful you've got to 'take hold of your brain's reins and focus on what's most important at the moment. For a hitter, the ball is what we call the 'critical variable.' That's a fancy way of saying the most important thing to focus on. When you're hitting great you're 100 percent focused on the ball. You don't have to think about what to do, you just do it.

"But when you're in a slump your focus is on your hands, your feet, your shoulders, your swing plane, your average, what the coach thinks, something else, or all of the above, and those interfere with your play."

"Agreed."

"Three other ways to say basically the same thing are: one, what you focus on you feel; two, what you focus on expands; and three, what you focus on you attract."

"What I focus on I feel?" I asked, processing it out loud.

"How do you feel when you focus on how badly you've hit lately?" said the man.

"Bad."

"Yes, and how about when you focus on that DL game?"

"Good."

"Okay, so what you focus on you feel. That's pretty important to know when feeling good is the name of the game, wouldn't you say?"

"For sure."

A quiz began: "So if you want to feel really good you focus on..."

"Something good. Something that makes you feel good."

"Yes. And if you want to feel bad..."

"Focus on something that makes you feel bad."

"Yes. And since how you feel corresponds to your vibration and you attract results and other events that are aligned with your vibration, what you choose to focus on is a really big deal."

"Got it."

"And that's what I mean by 'what you focus on expands.' It gets bigger in your life."

"I was thinking more of how the ball looks bigger and smaller sometimes," I said.

"Yes, exactly. Same thing. The ball obviously doesn't change size, but the way it occurs to you can change a great deal. A lot goes into that, including how deceptive the pitcher's delivery is, but if you're fully focused on the ball in a relaxed body the ball is going to look bigger than if you are tense and distracted."

"Because I'm focused on the ball instead of my mechanics or average."

"Yes. It gets bigger or you get more of it. So if you focus on how big a slump you're in, an even bigger slump is coming. If you focus on how big a jerk your coach is, he's going to become a bigger jerk. What you focus on expands."

"I see the pattern," I said. "But what if he really is a jerk?"

"Would it feel good to focus on that?"

"Good point," I said.

Feel Good and Focus

"Going back to our diagram," the man continued, "the target is to have a high vibe, ideally in The Bigs, and be fully focused on the target. I love putting things on a 0 to 10 scale, so we can do that with each line. Vibration first, where a 0 is fear and powerlessness and a 10 is freedom."

"I see," I said, "What would you say confidence was?"

"About an 8 or 9. But don't get hooked on exactly what emotions go with what numbers. Just focus on how 10 is high and 0 is low."

"I can certainly feel the difference."

"And focus ranges from 0 on the left where your head is in the clouds, to 10 on the right where you're laser focused on what you want."

"Cool."

"So you can plot yourself on the diagram. If you were a 7 on vibration and 8 on focus, you're at 7, 8 on the diagram."

"I see. I'd say my last AB yesterday, just before we met, I was about a 2, 3. I was in the lower left corner for sure."

"Yes."

"And this last AB I'd say I was a 6 or 7 vibe-wise going up there, but then crashed to a 2 or 3 after I swung at that breaking ball. My focus was about the same."

"You got it."

"And so my target is to be up here," I said, pointing with my bat to the upper right corner of the diagram. "In The Bigs with a high vibe and way to the right on the focus line."

"You got it," said the man.

"Simple enough," I said. ***"Feel good and focus."***

"Yes, especially since your vibe and your focus are so closely related. You pretty much move on a diagonal from upper right down toward the lower left."

"The less focused I am," I chimed in, "the lower my vibe is apt to be."

"Right. You're at your best when you're in the upper right corner, feeling good and focusing. That's when you'll be the freest and have the most access to your talent. Get there and you'll attract success like a magnet."

"But sometimes I play well and don't feel great," I said.

"That's because your focus made up for the lower vibe."

"I hit a few homers last year when I was scared of striking out. I'll bet I actually hit most of my homers with two strikes."

"Fear can work for you if you focus well. The ball really flies when you square it up, so if you direct the energy you got from your fear of striking out into simply hitting the ball you can do some real damage."

"Yes, that's weird. I hit the longest balls when I was just trying to hit the dang ball."

"Right on," the man laughed. "That's because you're designed for greatness."

"What do you mean?"

Questions to Consider for Part 5

1. How is the universe (and baseball) like a giant pitch back screen?

2. What is the one term that captures the key to success?

3. What are The Bigs as the man describes them?

4. What must you focus on to attract success like a magnet?

Download a full-size, printable copy of the Play Big "Feel Good and Focus" chart FREE at www.PlayBigTraining.com

Part 6:

"Why You So Rarely Play as Well as You Can (and how to change that)"

You're about to discover...

- **Why you're naturally great but play terribly**

- **The 2 enemies of excellence** *(knowing them is the first step to beating them)*

- **The REAL reason you feel fear and lose confidence** *(and what to do about it)*

- **The umpire that makes the most important calls in your life** *(almost no one even knows where he is!)*

- **How to play with total freedom** *(from fear, frustration, anger, etc.)*

Find out at:

PlayBigBaseball.com

The Truth about Great Performance

"The good news is the upper right corner is your natural place to be," the man continued. "As I mentioned earlier that's the real you. That's Big You. That's who's really on first. You true nature is to feel good. You also have a built in mechanism for focusing on targets. Your body functions best when you have a clear target."

"I'll need to think about that one," I said, "if it's so natural for me to be great..."

"Look," the man jumped in, "when you were a kid playing WIFFLE ball in the back yard, did you ever choke?"

"No," I said, "not that I can think of. Usually played awesome. I'd pretend I was Harmon Killebrew or Tony Oliva and I'd..."

"Exactly," said the man. "You had a great 'mental game' to start with. You didn't have a sport psychologist working with your WIFFLE ball team did you?"

"I can't remember one, no," I played along.

"Here's my point: You come pre-wired for excellence. That is, you're naturally good. You're naturally free to perform well. Yes, you must practice to be skilled, but when there's nothing in your way you crush it."

The corners of my lips turned up into a wistful smile as I recalled hammering WIFFLE ball homers over my best friend Fish's house. I was The Man back then.

"You know this already from your own experience," he said. "Don't you play really great sometimes in practice? In drills? Even in games? It might be happening randomly, but some days you're just great."

"For sure."

"Some might call it playing over your head, but I laugh at that phrase. You can't play better than you can play. It's like John Wooden used to say about how you can't give more than 100 percent. You can't play over your head. If you play at Level X one time you're capable of playing at Level X. But you don't normally play to that level because something gets in the way."

"Like what?"

"Well, here's a formula for it:
Performance = Potential – Interference.

"The formula says you will play to your potential, you'll play as well as you can play...except for whatever 'interference' gets in the way."

"I think I hear you."

"When you're playing great, is it hard or easy?

"Easy, of course," I said.

"That's because there's no interference. There's no resistance. There's nothing blocking you from playing to your potential that you have to overcome. You don't have to try hard because there's no weight to push. So you naturally play great, and the key to playing great is dramatically reducing or eliminating interference."

"What do you mean by interference?" I asked.

"Muscular tension and distraction are your two main forms of interference.

"When your muscles are tight you don't perform well. If you're throwing a ball and your fingers are clamped down tight on the ball that tension will reduce the speed and accuracy of the throw. If your bicep is tight when you're swinging a bat, that muscle is working against your swing, slowing it down."

I moved my arms slowly through a swing, noticing the role of the biceps.

"Your biceps pull your hand toward your shoulder," the man continued. "Thus it's not used in your swing. Your triceps are for extending your arm and are used in hitting. So any tension in your bicep when you are swinging 'interferes' with your swing."

"Got it," I said.

"So tension is your first form of interference. The other is distraction, or poor focus, and we covered that pretty well already."

"Performance follows focus," I said.

"Yes. Your body naturally finds effective ways to perform and get the job done when it has a clear target and is committed 100 percent to that target. When you don't have a clear target, like when you're focus is split between the ball and your hand position and your coach and your average and the girl you're sweet on in the stands, your performance suffers. That split focus is interference."

"Been there." *And how did he know about the girl in the stands?*

"Yes, so tension in your muscles and distractions in your head, each of these things is interference. They're getting in the way of your magnificent body and thus subtracting from your performance."

I chimed in:
"Performance = Potential – Interference."

"Yes. When you have no excess tension and you're totally focused on the critical variable (the most important thing such as the ball or your pitching target), you play to your potential."

I nodded.

"That's why the game can seem easier one day and harder the next," the man said. "When it's easier you have little to no tension and distraction. Remember, you're designed for excellence so if nothing is in your way you easily and natu-

rally play to your ability and skill level. By the way, 'ability' means natural talent, and 'skill' means capacity acquired through practice. Your potential at any given moment is the sum of the two."

"I see."

"When the game is hard you have unnecessary tension and/or you are distracted."

"I totally agree with all this about how great I am," I said in a playful tone, "and I agree that I get tense and lose focus under pressure. But to be honest with you, I basically knew that already. I couldn't have put it as clearly as you, but I did know that. I know I need to be relaxed and focused in order to play my best."

"Yes," said the man, knowing I was far from satisfied with what he'd said so far.

"The big question," I said, "is *Why!* Why do I do this to myself? If I'm designed for excellence, why don't I just play relaxed and focused all the time? We know that being relaxed, confident and focused on the critical variable gives us our best performances, so if our bodies are so smart and amazing, why do they get all negative? Wouldn't you think we would naturally just play great and not get all nervous and distracted?"

This time I wasn't surprised when the answer began with a history lesson...

Why You Get Nervous and Lose Confidence

"You're wonderfully designed," the man began. "In fact, you're absolutely incredible. Mind-bogglingly well designed. I do mean you specifically, 21, and I also mean all humans. It's really astonishing the level of complexity involved. You've got system upon system upon system that combine to create an absolute moment to moment miracle. From the coordination of the diaphragm muscles contracting and bringing air into your lungs and the lungs helping transfer the oxygen in the air to your blood cells that carry it. And then..."

"Okay," I cut in impatiently, "I get it. But now you're just piling on more and more reasons why I shouldn't get nervous, why I shouldn't get down on myself, and why I *shouldn't* screw up in the first place. I don't have all day here, why do I screw up? If I'm so amazingly designed, why do I get nervous and lose confidence?"

"There *is* one small problem with your design."

"Okay, now you're talking. What's the problem?"

"You're designed magnificently... but not for playing baseball."

"What?"

"You personally have some natural talent for the game and the more and better you practice the better you will be. But you, like all other players, all other humans, have a big engineering gap to fill before you can be a great player."

The man paused while we both watched Kamin throw a fastball strike to Thielen.

"Go on. If I'm not designed for baseball what am I designed so magnificently for?" I said. "What's the gap?"

"Great question. I'm only dragging out the answer because the answer is so important. Knowing what you're designed for, knowing your body's number-one priority explains a lot of things that happen in the game, and knowing it will simplify the game for you."

"I'm ready..."

"You're magnificently designed," said the man, "for survival. Safety is your body's top priority."

"Safety? How so?"

"Nothing else you can do matters if you're dead."

"True, go on."

"So your body's number-one priority is safety. Its top objective is to pass on your genes, to create future generations, to secure the survival of the species."

"Okay..."

"Your brain and the rest of your body are best designed to hunt and gather in tribes on the open plains of Africa, North America and elsewhere. Those were much more dangerous and primitive times. Real, life threatening things happened all the time. You're wonderfully designed for those activities."

"I'm not really seeing how this applies to baseball, but go on," I said.

"Here's how it works. Your mind is constantly processing the information that comes in through your senses. It's top priority is what?"

"Safety."

"Yes, so all the information that comes in is first processed by a part of your brain that assesses whether or not you're safe. I call that part of your brain your Inner Umpire."

"Oh, great," I said. "I've let umpires get in my head before, but I didn't know one lived in there."

"If your Inner Umpire decides, 'Yes, I'm safe,' then you have full access to your natural excellence. There's no interference. No muscle tension, no distraction. You're free to play big, to have a high vibration and attract all kinds of good stuff. Your energy expands when you feel free."

"Cool."

"But if it decides 'No, I'm not safe, GET OUT! — it sets off alarms and your freedom is revoked. You can only do any one or a combination of three things: fight for your life, run for your life, or freeze and hope the bad guys don't see you."

"None of those sound good for my game," I said.

"Correct" said the man. "They're all about protection and contracting. Low vibration stuff. When you fight or run for your life all the blood rushes from your smaller muscles to your big muscles. Energy is taken from your brain to reinforce your big muscles."

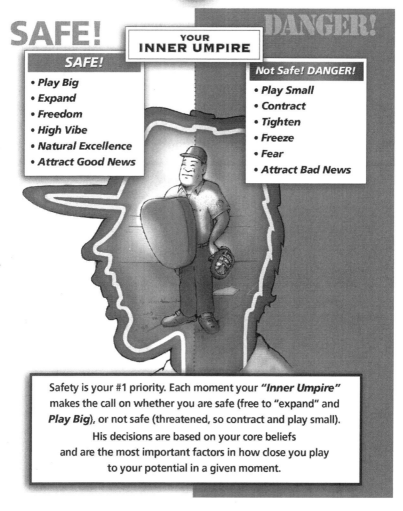

Your Inner Umpire

SAFE! **DANGER!**

SAFE!
- *Play Big*
- *Expand*
- *Freedom*
- *High Vibe*
- *Natural Excellence*
- *Attract Good News*

Not Safe! DANGER!
- *Play Small*
- *Contract*
- *Tighten*
- *Freeze*
- *Fear*
- *Attract Bad News*

Safety is your #1 priority. Each moment your *"Inner Umpire"* makes the call on whether you are safe (free to "expand" and *Play Big*), or not safe (threatened, so contract and play small). His decisions are based on your core beliefs and are the most important factors in how close you play to your potential in a given moment.

"That's why I do stupid things when I'm nervous?"

"Yes, that's why you get stupid: blood and energy literally leave your brain. You also contract your muscles to brace for attack. You tighten and collapse around your chest to protect your heart and other vital organs. Your attention narrows, but not in a good way: You block out everything that doesn't seem related to the threat. You block out im-

181

portant information and instead focus on things that seem important to your unconscious mind but aren't important to baseball."

"Like 'don't strike out' instead of focusing on the ball."

"Yes. Your fear can cause you to block out the ball. Not good for the batting average. And when you freeze, you freeze! You know how when you're tight at the plate you don't breathe well?"

"Yes."

"Stopping your breath is part of the 'freeze' response. You stop moving so no monsters or bad guys see you."

"That seems ridiculous. There are no monsters or bad guys here."

"The key variable is the perception of danger – a decision made by an unconscious belief. You don't make a choice in the moment about what you perceive as dangerous and what you perceive as safe any more than you choose what call an umpire makes on the field."

"They certainly don't get 'em all right."

"True. An umpire's call is not what actually happened; it's what he believes happened. Very big difference. The better the umpire, the closer his calls are to facts."

"So if my Inner Umpire is crappy he gets a lot of calls wrong?"

"YES!" said the man. "Excellent. If your Inner Umpire is constantly saying you're in danger, GET OUT! when you're

really safe, you'll play well below your potential. You'll constantly be tight, nervous, scared, protecting yourself and contracting when you don't need to be."

"That's me."

"You're right: the fact is you aren't in any real life threatening danger – except if a ball is coming at your head, of course. *But the facts aren't what are important.* Even when you aren't in any real danger, that 'fact' doesn't matter; what matters is how your Inner Umpire sees the situation."

"If he thinks I'm in danger he hits the panic button," I said to make sure I had it right.

"Yes."

"And if he calls me safe I'm free to be Mr. Wonderful that you described before."

"You got it."

I watched Kamin throw a high and tight fastball past Joe Knight. We didn't get Kamin early, and now we're seeing him get stronger as the game goes on.

The man continued: "Society has advanced fast these past hundreds of years and our internal wiring hasn't kept up. You can know rationally you aren't in a life-threatening situation, but remember, we're run 95 percent by our non-conscious minds. So rational thought doesn't play as big a role in our lives as we think it does."

"So it's all about fear," I said.

"Yes, because it's all about safety," said the man. "When you believe you're safe, you're free and have full access to your talents and skills. When you believe your well-being is at risk you go caveman, tighten up and get cut off from your greatness. Your priority is fighting off a killer, running from one, or freezing so still that a predator won't see you."

"Hmm," I grunted, taking it all in. "Okay, but help me out here: What's the threat in striking out? Why is that such a big deal? I'm not in any physical danger. It's embarrassing, yes, even humiliating. But not dangerous."

"Good one," said the man. "Here's my take on that. Early man lived in tribes. We needed to for safety and division of labor. There was safety in numbers – you can better fight off predators with a group of people than by yourself."

I nodded.

"Hunting food is much easier in a group than by yourself when you're using spears and rocks to kill things."

"True."

"So you needed others around you to survive. If you did something that upset the tribe and got kicked out you were in big trouble. Getting kicked out of the tribe was essentially a death sentence. And likely an unpleasant death at that. Going solo was lonely and deadly."

"Makes sense," I said before asking, "so I'm wired to fear being cast out of the tribe?"

"If you were cast out of the tribe it was almost a death sentence because you needed 'teammates' to hunt with and

protect against predators. Deep within us is a drive to belong, to fit in, and to be social. That's why most everyone
today cares so much about what others think of them.
*We have an innate fear of being outcast. Playing poorly
taps into that fear."*

"So I get nervous and lose confidence because I'm afraid I
might get kicked out of the tribe?" I said.

"Yes."

"But getting nervous and scared that I might get kicked out
of the tribe makes it more likely I'll play badly... and get
kicked out of the tribe!"

"Funny, isn't it?" said the man.

"Pretty messed up if you ask me."

"Yes, that's what I meant by you aren't designed to play
baseball; you're designed for survival. The engineering gap
I referred to is that while your natural state is freedom and
greatness, your top priority is safety. So protection trumps
freedom and you play badly when you're in protection
mode."

"So what do I do about that?" I said. "How can I stay in
freedom mode?"

"Upgrade your Inner Umpire."

"How so?"

"Train your Inner Umpire, which is really your belief system,
so that it knows striking out doesn't mean death. That making

an error, while not being fun, isn't the end of the world. Understanding, no, more than understanding, KNOWING in each and every one of your cells that you're safe no matter what happens in today's game. You're a good and worthy man no matter what happens on this next pitch.

"Your cells must each be certain that 'I'm okay no matter what happens' and that the game is just a game. Something to enjoy.' And that baseball is a vehicle for you to enjoy yourself and expand yourself," said the man, "not a courtroom where your worth is on trial."

"But I know this isn't life or death," I said.

"Your upper brain does, but your mid-brain, lower brain and the rest of your body don't. If your whole body – and your brain is part of your body, of course – completely knew you were okay no matter what happened you would be excited and eager to play, not scared. You'd have excitement pumping through your veins, not anxiety. And you wouldn't have to come out of the dugout to blow off steam when you struck out. In other words, you would have never met me."

I nodded.

> "Now, it's time for you to go get ready to hit.
> We've covered a lot, but it really boils down
> to two ideas: Feel good and focus.
>
> "Feeling good is about raising your vibration,
> getting to The Bigs or as close as you can so your
> energy flows freely and the Law of Attraction
> can bring you good things.
>
> "Focus is about directing your energy flow
> out at the ball. You can't hit the ball if your energy isn't
> connected to it. Your ABCs help you do all that."

It was still hard for me to imagine that I could feel so bad for two weeks, still not have a hit in decades, but feel excited and confident about my next showdown with Kamin.

It's all coming together on this at-bat, I told myself.

How to Have a Great At-Bat

I felt like I'd just crammed for an exam. We'd covered a ton of information and I was at risk of thinking too much about too many things. But I remembered our core principle: simple wins.

I began talking to myself: *If you remember one term the man had said, remember "vibrational match." Everything revolves around that one idea. Become a vibrational match for great hitting.*

**What you focus on you vibrate so
what you focus on you attract.**

Okay, okay, too much. Stay with the basics, remember, despite all the ideas we've covered it still comes down to doing my ABCs. The Play Big ABCs raise my vibration.

Act Big.

Breathe Big.

Commit Big.

I paused in front of our bat rack and took a big breath and lifted my head and shoulders. Slow and steady. I took the bat in my hands and ran my hand up the length of it. I looked at the fat part, the sweet spot of the bat. I brushed my fingers across it and thought to myself: see the ball and hit it right there.

Act Big. I deliberately put my helmet on, and then confidently strode up the dugout steps and into the on-deck area.

Breathe Big. I drew a long, slow breath into my belly. As I exhaled I bent forward to stretch my back and hamstrings. It was pretty common for me to tighten up back there as a game went on and today was no exception. I felt the muscles let go as my breath left my body. I lifted slightly as I drew another full breath to my stomach, and easily dropped further into the stretch as I let it go.

Commit Big. Forget everything that's happened before, just focus on seeing the ball and putting the fat part of the bat on it. That was good enough for Hall of Famers like Aaron and Musial, so it's good enough for me.

I transported myself back to DL. The man's voice led me: "See what you saw… hear what you heard… and feel how good that feels to be totally and unstoppably confident."

Ah, that DL at-bat. Like a good friend it picked me up again. I saw it, heard it and began to feel it. This was fun, I enjoyed this feeling. And imagine, I feel confident but haven't gotten a hit in years!

Was I as confident and locked in as I was in DL? No way. But I felt good. *It's not about feeling perfect or trying to exactly re-create DL, it's about feeling good.*

And I felt good.

I also liked the way the inning felt, especially after Swenson singled. As Dotseth took on Kamin, I went through my Green Light Routine pretending I was facing Kamin. I even stepped out between pitches, and took my breath and stepped back into my imaginary batter's box.

Dots walked, putting runners on first and second.

"Here we go."

I held my head and chest up as I walked to the plate. This was my time and I was going to take it. My heart beat sped up with each step as I walked tall behind the umpire and I could feel myself starting to contract. But I took my time,

kept breathing, and when I got to the batter's box, I wiped it clean with my right foot, clearing out the footprints of previous hitters, making it my own.

I was enjoying it. The blood was pumping, and a ton of energy was vibrating my body. I could feel everyone's eyes on me, but everything was happening at a pace I was comfortable with. My head was clear enough to remember my routine and my ABCs.

No signs from the third base coach. I planted my right foot in the back of the box, took a breath in, and planted my left foot as I exhaled.

See the ball and put the fat part on it. See the ball and put the fat part on it. I rocked forward and back, forward and back.

Kamin rocked back and fired. I rocked back and swu—NO! I saw the tumbling action just in time. Kamin was trying to get me to chase another curveball right away, but this time I saw it and held up.

Ball one.

Nice to be ahead in the count. I felt good. Green light.

I went back to my Green Light routine. Stepped in big, breathed big, committed big.

Kamin rocked back and fired. I rocked back and... saw a slightly different spin... change up. But again I saw it and again it was out of the strike zone.

Ball two.

Good stuff. My teammates loved it. I don't know if they sensed my energy was different, but I sure did.

Man, I love this feeling.

Green light. *Careful not to get too amped up now and swing for the fences. My commitment is to see the ball and put the fat part on it, not hit it to Fargo.*

Green Light Routine. I executed it smoothly, easily, deliberately.

Kamin got his sign, rocked and fired. I saw the ball, a fastball, streaking toward the plate, but it was one of those times when it seems like all the information coming in and going out by-pass your brain. I swung without thinking. I swung without tensing. I swung without really knowing I was swinging.

PING!

The pitch was headed for the inner half of the plate when the fat part of my bat radically changed the ball's flight plan. Instead of strike one, the ball was on a line to left-center.

I raced toward first and heard the wind rushing over the ear holes of my helmet. The ball landed between the outfielders and skidded to the fence. Everyone was running somewhere at full speed. I veered into the grass to the right of first base to set up my angle to second. I knew Swense was on his way home to tie the game, the only question was if Dots, the team slow-poke, could get in to give us the lead.

A slight bobble by the center fielder as he picked up the ball sealed the deal and I cruised into second clapping my hands and turning to watch Dots lumber in.

Man, I love this feeling.

Nothing quite like feeling your foot resting safely on a well-earned base. Especially when it's been a while and you just put your team ahead. Of course I kept a calm, cool, I-do-this-all-the-time look on my face, but inside I was dancing.

That was all we could get that inning – I never left second base.

But as I threw ground balls to my infielders between innings I basked in the glow of my success. I really enjoyed myself.

I glanced over to the shadowy blob behind the wind-screen by our dugout and raised my chin, a salute to the man I knew was there. It was a fulfilling moment. Getting a hit is always fun, but I'd overcome a lot to get that one. And the man was right, overcoming challenges felt good deep down.

I'd enjoyed myself and expanded myself. *"What a coincidence,"* I smiled, *"that's why I play the game in the first place."*

But my joy was short lived. The Rakeops' first three batters produced a single, a walk and a two-run double.

We now trailed 3-2.

Questions to Consider for Part 6

1. What are you best designed for?
   In other words, what is your body's
   #1 priority?

2. What are the two main forms of
   "interference?" (Knowing them is the
   first step to beating them)

3. What is the "Inner Umpire" and what "calls"
   does he make?

4. What does it mean to "upgrade your
   Inner Umpire?"

Download a full-size, printable copy
of the Play Big "Feel Good and Focus"
chart FREE at
www.PlayBigTraining.com

IF YOU DON'T PLAY OR COACH BASEBALL...

PLAY BIG is much more than a baseball book. The powerful ideas in PLAY BIG can also help you…

- **Double your effectiveness at work**
- **Increase your income exponentially**
- **Finally lose the weight and get into good physical shape**
- **Create the relationships of your dreams**
- **Be more happy and fulfilled!**

Go now to *www.PlayBigTraining.com* to get "life" versions of

- **The ABC exercise**
- **"Feel Good and Focus Chart" download**
- **Tapping Video to Remove Stress and Fear (tap along with me and see what the excitement is all about)**
- **And much more…. FREE!**

All the knowledge in this book will go to waste
if you don't take action. All great performers have coaches.

Get yours now FREE at
www.PlayBigTraining.com

©2011 Dr. Tom Hanson

Part 7:

"How to Play Big in 5 Simple Steps"

You're about to discover...

- **What MUST be your top priority if you want success AND peace of mind**

- **Why you cannot let "reality" rule your world**

- **Which comes first, success or confidence?**

- **How to Play Big (the 5-step model)**

How to Raise Your Vibration

We got out of the inning without further damage, but had just two more innings to catch up.

I shook my head as I stepped outside the dugout. My hitting heroics had been trumped by the Rakeops 3-run blast. "Baseball sure is a game of contrast," I said.

"It sure is," he replied. "Just when you think you have the game by the tail something happens that sets you straight. If he's not careful a guy's vibration can go on a roller coaster ride during just one inning."

"No doubt," I said. "I still feel great about my AB, though. What did you think of it?"

"Doesn't matter what I think, just tune in to how you feel. Your feelings are your guide. Focus on your relationship with your feelings."

"You sound like Yoda again."

"He's a smart little troll. But what question do you have now?"

"What do you mean?"

"After what you've learned there's only one relevant question to ask."

I thought for a moment: What question do I have? Actually, what's the only question I should have?

"Well," I said, "I really had fun that at-bat. I guess you'd say my vibration was pretty high."

"Yes," the man interrupted, "and remember, just because you feel good it doesn't mean you'll get a hit every time. Baseball and the Law of Attraction never let you down, but they don't always give you want you want the moment you want it."

"I know I can't get a hit every time, but I want to do it more. I want to be better at this so I don't go through what I went through these past two weeks. So I guess my question would be about how to get better at this stuff. You've mentioned practice, *how do I practice it? What do I practice?*"

"Yes," said the man.

Your New Top Priority

The man seemed excited that I'd asked him how to practice these techniques he's been teaching me.

"Quiz time," the man began. "I've said if you only remember one idea that captures this whole Play Big idea, what is it?"

"Vibrational match."

"Right. High vibes bring good news."

"And low vibes bring crap," I interjected.

The man chuckled. "You could put it that way, yes. And I said if you only remember one thing to do, what is it?"

"You mean the ABCs?"

"Yes, but the ABCs help you..."

"Feel good and focus."

"Yes. Feel good, or great if it's within reach, and focus."

"Got it."

"So here's your new top priority: Feel Good. The Bigs. Instead of thinking something has to happen in order for you to feel good – like you have to get a hit or win a game or get some coach's approval – generate feeling good first.

"Almost every player has it backwards. They think they'll feel good when they have success. But great players, consistent players, create good feelings out of thin air because they know good feelings lead to good results."

"Like a magician," I said.

"Yes. Make getting to The Bigs your top priority every day. It might seem radical or even cheesy to some, but every player already knows the power of it. They know they play better and enjoy the game more when they feel good. They just don't connect the dots. They don't put two and two together and come to the logical conclusion that *in order to play great consistently they need to get good at feeling good before anything happens in the so-called 'real' world."*

"I see," I said. "It still seems sort of strange. But I can't see myself hitting that double without changing my focus the way you did."

"If you play baseball and need something good to happen to you before you feel good, you're in trouble."

"Because not much good will happen to you unless you feel good?" I said.

"Excellent. Remember: vibrational match."

"Okay," I said, "I'm on board. But how? How do I get myself to feel good before anything happens? I know we've covered the ABC's, which did wonders for me. But what else?"

"You remember our patron saint Dr. Semmelweis?"

"Sure."

"Realizing what was really going on – in his case germs – led him to washing his hands after working with dead people. Now that we know what's really going on in baseball – that everything is energy and it follows the Law of Attraction – there are several things you can do to raise your vibration."

Which Comes First, Success or Confidence?

"Focusing is directing your energy," the man began, "so the more accurate question is 'How and what should I focus on to raise my vibration?'"

"Got it," I said.

"First and most important," said the man, "is simply to be aware of your feelings and how important they are to your success."

"I hear you," I said, "I mean, I feel you."

"You'll remember our basic motto that summarizes everything you need to do to Play Big is 'feel good and …'"

"Focus?"

"Yes, feel good and focus. That's what it all boils down to. Feel good so the Law of Attraction brings you good stuff, and focus so your energy is directed in the most effective way. No matter how you feel, Commit Big."

"A big one for me to remember is to focus on what I want instead of what I don't want."

"That's right. Some players will make an out and then spend all their time before their next at-bat focusing their energies on the out they made (something they don't want to do again), instead of on what they do want, such as driving the ball hard to the outfield."

"That's so stupid," I said, joining the man in mocking me about focusing on making an out.

"Your focus is your main tool for raising your vibration. Find something to focus on that makes you feel just a little bit better."

"In that first ABC exercise you took me through yesterday you shifted my focus from how I was 2 for 20 and had just struck out, to a time when I hit great."

"Yes. And now just think, you're 3-for-22!"

"I'd rather not think about that," I laughed.

"That's exactly right. The only people who want you to think about that are the Rakeops and their fans. You're only helping them by focusing your energy on what you don't want."

"Never thought of it that way," I said. "I'm good now, though. Funny how a smoked double can turn a guy's feelings around."

"Yes, but that's not what happened. You turned yourself around before the double. You wouldn't have doubled without it; the Law of Attraction wouldn't have allowed it."

"That's true. The double feels to me like the result that came from my turning myself around. But it's tough to break out of the habit of thinking that my feelings are controlled by what happens instead of the other way around."

"You'll never break your connection to results totally. So be sure not to beat yourself up over caring about results. Just notice when you're focused on results and turn north. Focus on The Bigs. Focus on your feelings. Remember they're your GPS, your Greatness Positioning System. Your feelings will tell you when you aren't aligned with who you really are."

"Got it."

"So again, what you focus on you feel, so one way to raise your vibration is to focus on something that makes you feel good. And then keep focusing on it."

I nodded.

"Remember," said the man, "What you focus on you feel. The Law of Attraction brings you results and experiences consistent with your vibration.

"How you feel equals your vibration, so the key to success is to use your free will to intentionally direct your focus to things that make you feel good."

"Okay," I said, "what do I focus on to feel good?"

How to Play Big

At that moment we were feeling pretty good as a team. Although Kamin was still in the game, we'd been hitting the ball better against him than we had all summer. Maybe we'd finally have his number today. Of course, we were still trailing. At that moment, knowing I should get at least one more crack at Kamin, I wanted to find out from the man how I could feel good.

(I'd given up wondering why it seemed like I had so much time to talk to the man.)

"Step one is to clarify what you don't want," he said.

"What I *don't* want?"

"Yes."

"Why would I do that? I thought you were all about focusing my energy north, toward feeling good."

"Just as when you throw you bring your arm back to generate tension and space to more powerfully sling the ball forward, focusing on what you don't want generates tension and space for you to rocket forward toward what you do want."

"I see... I think."

"Focusing on what you don't want creates contrast. Contrast builds energy, like stretching a rubber band. When you're in the middle there's no momentum, no stretch. When you clarify what you don't want it creates an equal and opposite energy toward what you do want."

"Okay," I argued, "but that's easier said than done. You can sit here and say 'think happy thoughts' but it's another thing to do it when you haven't had a hit in a month."

"The challenge is to not let the reality around you dominate your thoughts and feelings. Just because you aren't getting what you want doesn't mean you can't or won't. It just means you're at step one, that's all. Don't stop there! Go to step two."

"What's step two?"

"Clarify what you do want."

"That's more like it."

"Yes, use that knowledge or experience of what you don't want to catapult your focus toward what you do want. It happens almost automatically. In fact, you're feeling bad because you have a clear idea that what you're getting doesn't match up with what you want. So you must know what you want in order for that to happen. Step two is just to clarify what you want as best you can."

"Alright, that makes some sense."

"Your problem is you're really good at step one; you habitually focus on what you don't want."

"Nice to be good at something!" I said sarcastically.

"Yes, but you don't want to be a step one expert. Most players are. They focus on what they don't want. That's what drew me to offer my help to you: you were stuck in step one but I could see you were coachable."

"Cool. I do love this psychology stuff. And it's usually pretty simple. That's why I'm going to major in it."

"Most players aren't open to talking about anything that's going on inside them. They're stuck in thinking it's all about their mechanics and physical strength and think the keys to the kingdom are there."

"But mechanics and conditioning are important," I said.

HOW TO

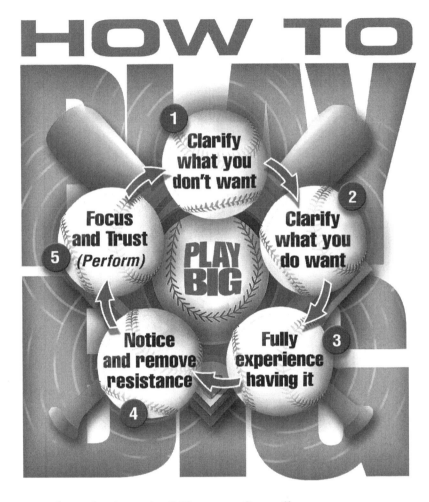

1. Clarify what you don't want
2. Clarify what you do want
3. Fully experience having it
4. Notice and remove resistance
5. Focus and Trust (Perform)

PLAY BIG

"Yes, but that's sort of like spending all your money on a big fancy TV and not saving any money for your electric bill. Energy is the power source. If you don't have power running into your TV you're going to be disappointed with your big purchase. If you don't pay attention to your personal energy you're going to be disappointed with your baseball career."

"So I want the TV and the power source?"

"Yes. And start with the power source. It's what makes everything else possible. And the way to do it is to first clarify what you don't want. What do you not want?"

"I don't want to strike out. I don't want to be a loser when my team needs me the most. I don't want to feel like a douche."

"Okay," smiled the man, enjoying the clarity in my negativity. "What *do* you want?"

"I want to rip the ball. I want to run the bases. I want to have fun playing."

"Okay, now step three is to experience getting what you want. This is what we did in that first exercise where I had you re-experience the DL game. You went back there and saw what you saw, heard what you heard, and felt what you felt when you were totally and unstoppably confident."

"Yes," I said, "I love that feeling."

"Exactly. That's what I want you to get: that you love that feeling and that feeling is your target. That's what you want because it feels good and…"

"And it helps me play my best, and gives me my best chance of winning," I finished.

"Yes. Now it's not going to be all magic-like and woo-woo zone feeling all the time, maybe never. That's not what I'm talking about. I'm talking about playing with how good you can feel right now. And enjoying what feeling good feels like today. Go north. ***Always reach for the highest vibration thought and feeling you can right now.***"

"Got it."

"And going to the past is a great way to do it. The easiest. It's easier to remember feeling great for most people than to generate it about the future out of thin air. So you can start generating the feeling by going to your past, but step three is to put yourself in the future and experience what it will be like when you get what you want."

"Like having a DL experience for this next at-bat?"

"Exactly. And it's as basic as just imagining you're there. See what you'll see, hear what you'll hear and feel what you'll feel when you have the at-bat you want."

"Okay," I said, my body beginning to sway as I transported myself to the batter's box and started feeling good."

"Your ABCs will always guide you there," the man continued. "They're just the tip of the iceberg for what I could teach you about how to feel good, but we don't have much time. Let's see if we can discover step four."

"Okay."

"Imagine yourself going up there now and having a great at-bat, getting what you want. Now tell me this: how confident do you feel?"

I paused for a moment, tuning in my mind to seeing a great at-bat. "About a seven," I said.

"And that's normal. Welcome to step four. As you imagine yourself accomplishing your goal or getting what you want it's common to feel good but not great. Normally you'll have some negative feeling that comes with it."

"That's stupid. Why would that be?"

"Your inner umpire is, for some reason, seeing it as not safe. He just doesn't believe fully you can do it and there's some risk in even trying for it. So step four is to notice and remove your resistance to success."

"Okay, but I still don't get why I'd resist success. Why would I?"

"That feeling is a signal that somehow you're not safe. It's that very feeling, which is generated by a core belief, that's keeping you from getting what you want in the first place. If you didn't have that negative feeling when you connected with success you would either have achieved it by now or be flying towards it, resistance-free."

"Oh," I said, "I think that actually makes sense."

"Remember, you're wired for excellence, for freedom, for free energy flow. But your top priority is safety and your core beliefs can cause you to see things in such a way that it's dangerous for you to achieve what you want."

"The Inner Umpire."

"Yes, for most players he's the inner vampire, sucking the energy out of their dreams."

"That's pretty vivid. I know *I've* sucked a lot these past two weeks. How do I get rid of that?"

"To really do it we'd need much more time. We'd need to do some Play Big Training. But I think we'll have time to give

you a brief experience of it that should help free you up a bit."

"Let's do it," I said as time just seemed to be suspended.

"Okay, but let's finish out the model first. The goal at step four is to reduce your resistance as much as possible before it's time to perform. Once it's time to perform you're at step five, which is to focus and trust."

"It always comes back to focus, doesn't it?" I said.

"Yes. Everything is energy, and focus is how you control your energy, so it's a pretty big deal."

"And trust?"

"Trust means let go. Let your energy pour out onto the field and onto your target. It's the opposite of holding on. When you've got doubts and worries you contract, you hold on and try to control things outside of your control. When you're free you let go. That's trust."

"Got it. I know I hit best when I trust my hands instead of thinking about it."

"Yes, and instead of trying. Trust is the opposite of trying."

"I see."

"So regardless of how successful you are at clearing your resistance to success in Step 4, you focus and trust what you've got. You go out and do your ABCs."

"Cool."

"Then there's a good chance that sooner or later, usually sooner, something is going to happen that you don't want. Then, instead of throwing a drama queen fit, you can say 'Oh, I'm back at step one,' and you go around the circle again."

"So this can be done in sort of a formal training session..."

"Yes."

"But it also is like an ongoing thing," I said. "Like any time I feel myself not liking how I feel I can start at step one and go through it."

"Right on. But let's go back to step four and see if we can get some of that resistance cleared out before your next, and probably last, at-bat."

Questions to Consider for Part 7

1. What MUST be your top priority if you want success AND peace of mind?

2. What is your main tool for raising your vibration?

3. Which comes first, success or confidence?

4. Why is it helpful to clarify what you don't want?

Download a full-size, printable copy of the Play Big "Feel Good and Focus" chart and more training materials FREE at **www.PlayBigTraining.com**

Part 8:

"How to Tap Your Full Potential"

You're about to discover...

- How to quickly and easily eliminate fear and frustration

- When positive thinking is the WRONG thing to do

- The most powerful performance enhancement tool available

- How to train yourself to be calm and confident when the game is on the line

How to Tap Your Full Potential

"Say this out loud: 'I'm an awesome hitter and I'm about to have a great at-bat.'"

"I'm an awesome hitter and I'm about to have a great at-bat."

"How true does that feel? Say it again, and this time pause to feel it and then give me a zero to 10 on how true that feels, where 10 is totally true and zero is totally false."

"I'm an awesome hitter and I'm about to have a great at-bat."

I gave it a moment to sink in. I still was juiced from my double, but I had to say there remained some doubt in there rattling around. I had one pretty bad ABs today and a bunch more these past two weeks and they weren't out of my system yet.

"Seven," I finally blurted out.

"How do you know? What do you feel, hear or see that makes it a seven instead of a 10?"

"Well," I said as I scanned my body. "I just feel a little tension in my chest. And I saw an image of my strike out yesterday flash through my mind. I mean, I feel good, that double helped a lot. But I guess I felt a little contraction of my energy, as you'd say, as I said the sentence."

"Great. Nice awareness. ***The ability to feel your feelings and know what's going on inside you is the gateway to all success.***"

Tapping into any more of my full potential was going to have to wait. The Rakeops ended our inning. Kamin and his teammates still held a one-run lead as we took the field for the top of the sixth inning.

As much as I talk about the game Kamin was pitching, Dorigan was doing just as well for us. In fact, he had an incredible sixth. You don't see many five-pitch innings, but Dorigan gave us one. Evidently the Rakeops were eager to hit with their one-run lead. After back-to-back fly outs to Finanger in right field, another fly ball – this time to Swenson in left, ended the inning.

Much like the Rakeops hitters were eager to swing in the sixth, I couldn't wait to get back to the man at the fence to see how I could feel more like I did on my double. Especially since, if we were going to have a chance to win it, I'd get another chance to hit today.

How to Quickly and Easily Clear out Negative Thoughts and Feelings

"Okay," said the man, "think more about that strike out yesterday and feel that tension and contraction in your chest," the man instructed me. "How strong is it, zero to 10, where 10 it's super strong and zero it's gone?"

I instinctively took a breath to help me tune in to it. "I'd say about a four or five. It's definitely there, but nowhere near as bad as I felt right after it."

"Okay, great. We can only deal with the present moment, so we focus on what you feel now as you re-experience it, not what you felt back then."

"Yeah, I'd say about a four or five right now."

"This technique I'll share with you now is pretty strange. The good news is you don't have to believe in it for it to work. It's not some placebo that depends on you thinking it will work. So, you can doubt it and make fun of it all you want. My only request is that you try it."

"You've shared some awesome stuff with me so far, and even though a lot of it seemed pretty odd at first, each time it's ended up being great, so I'll play along."

"Okay. It's simply called tapping. It's called that because that's what you do: you physically tap on particular spots on your body."

"Um, you're right, that is weird. But go on."

"Keep your feeling of tension and contraction in your mind, along with that image of you striking out. Now, take your index, middle and ring fingers of either hand, but let's say your right hand, and start tapping with them on your right eyebrow. Slide your fingers toward the center of your face so your middle finger is tapping right where your eyebrow begins."

"The beginning meaning closest to my nose?"

"Yes. Middle finger on that inside edge of your eyebrow. And start tapping, like you're tapping on keys on a keyboard. Tap hard enough that you feel it, and not so hard that you hurt yourself. And you're tapping about three taps per second. But don't worry about counting them or how fast your doing it, just do it."

I could see enough of the man to get a sense of where and how he was tapping. It seemed easy enough so far, but I wondered how the heck this would help me hit.

"Like this?" I said, tapping away.

"Yes. This is basically a relaxation technique, so be relaxed about how you're doing. The technique is enormously forgiving, meaning you don't have to be precise with it, there's a large margin for error."

"Sounds like my kind of technique."

"Indeed. Next move to the right side of your right eye. Let your ring finger feel the edgy bone of your eye socket. You aren't all the way back to your temple."

"Tapping."

"Third is just below the eye, so you're tapping about an inch below your pupil. You'll again feel that eye socket bone... good. You're tapping for two or three seconds on each spot, just tap, tap, tap, tap."

"Got it," I said.

"Fourth is just below the nose, right on your mustache if you had one.

"Fifth is just below your lower lip, in that concave little divot. Not all the way down to your chin. Sort of right on the gums of your lower teeth.

"Next is called the collarbone point, but it's really just below where your collar bone starts in the center of your chest. If you start your fingers on your collar bone at your shoulders and then slide them in until you feel it end and drop away, drop down about an inch below that point where it ends and tap right there."

"Right here?"

"Yes. And with any of these you can tap on either side of your body – like on either eyebrow or eye, or either collarbone."

"Cool."

"Next point is four inches under your arm pit. Right on your bra strap if you have one of those on."

"No, not today, sorry."

"Good. Tapping would help you with that issue but we don't have that kind of time," the man said with a laugh.

I smiled. I'd really come to enjoy this guy, whoever he was. He said he could see himself in me; I'd like to grow up to be more like him.

"Now I also like to tap spots on your fingers," he continued. "Hold your right hand just in front of you, elbow bent, with

your thumb pointed up like you're going to shake someone's hand. Now tap on the left side of your right thumb, right in the middle of the last segment of your thumb."

"Here?"

"Yes. Right in line with the base of your thumb nail. You aren't on your thumb nail because you're on the side of your thumb, but if the base of your thumb nail was extended you'd be right on it."

"Got it."

"Sometimes I just tap with one or two fingers on these finger spots."

"Okay," I said, tap, tap, tapping on the side of my thumb.

"Now, move to the same spot on the thumb side of your index finger. Right, in the middle of the side of that last segment of your pointer finger, in line with the base of your thumb nail."

"Got it."

"And now the same spot on your middle finger…tap, tap, tap, tap, tap, tap… and then your ring finger… tap, tap, tap, tap, tap… and your pinky finger,… tap, tap, tap, tap, tap. Good. And finally on the very top of your head. Tap or flutter your fingers lightly on the very crown of your head. Excellent."

"Does it matter if I have my hat on?"

"Nope, that's fine. So that's one round of tapping. You start

on your eyebrow and work all the way around to your head and then start again at your eyebrow. I like to call it a 'tap lap.'"

"Easy enough. But this does what for me again?"

"We'll find out in a moment. Now that you know the spots we can move quicker and focus on your emotions much more. So focus back on that tightness in your chest, that contracting feeling you mentioned, and let's do a few more tap laps."

"Okay."

"Start tapping on your eyebrow point, remember it's scooted in toward the center of your face a bit, and really now focus on that tightness in your chest, that constriction. Tap on your eyebrow point... now the side of your eye...below your eye... that's it, focus on that constriction in your chest and breathe and tap... now below your nose... under your lip... under your collar bone... under your arm..."

"On the bra strap?"

"Yes," the man said and I could tell he was smiling again. "And now the side of the thumb... index finger... middle finger...ring finger... pinky... and the top of your head. Good. Now again. Start back on the eyebrow. And as you tap now really picture that tension in your chest, really feel that doubt, that fear, that you won't have a good at-bat. That's it, move right on through the spots, tapping a couple of seconds or so on each spot, and really focus on that doubt, on that tension."

"This obviously isn't one of those positive thinking techniques."

"No, it's not," the man laughed. "I call it a 'put your head in the mouth of the dragon' approach. Instead of pretending your fears and doubts and frustrations aren't there, you deal with reality and take them on. I'll explain that more in a moment. Just stay focused on your doubts and fears and how much you've stunk the past two weeks."

"Great, thank you."

"No problem. Really see that strike out image flash through your head and keep tapping and breathing, tapping and breathing."

"Focused on the negative...?"

"Focused on the negative."

I did what the man said, but it seemed to be just the opposite of what I would want to do: *Why focus on the negative? Isn't that just stirring it all up again? Wasn't that going against what he talked about earlier? I was feeling pretty good after that double, why dig up the negative thinking again?*

"Tapping works on whatever you're focused on. It releases it. So to clear out the negative you focus on it and tap."

"If you say so."

"I do."

I completed a third complete tap lap, focused on the constriction in my chest and the image of me striking out.

"Stop tapping now and take a nice deep breath in through
your nose and hold it in your belly... And then exhale let the
breath go."

It felt good to let that breath go. It felt like it took something out
of me with it, something I was happy to feel go.

"Now," said the man. "Say this out loud: I'm an awesome
hitter and I'm going to have a great at-bat."

"I'm an awesome hitter and I'm going to have a great at-bat."

"How true does that feel, zero to 10?"

I paused for a moment to check in with myself.

"Actually," I said, hesitating so I could double check my as-
sessment of how I felt, "I'd say a strong eight, maybe even a
nine. That's weird."

"Yes. And tune in to your chest, what's the tension level there,
zero to 10, with zero being it's gone."

"I'd have to say maybe a three."

"Okay, so now..."

"Why is that?" I jumped in. "I just focused on all these negative things and I just got more confident and less tense?"

"Told you it was weird, but let's keep going, we're going to
run out of time before you need to get ready to hit."

"What's next?"

"Do one more lap, and this time repeat to yourself, 'This remaining tension in my chest, this remaining doubt, this remaining tension in my chest, this remaining doubt.'"

I again did as I was told. I watched Kamin nearly throw another fastball Finanger couldn't handle, fouling it back over our heads.

After the lap, the man said: "Take a deep breath in through your nose and hold it in your belly.... And exhale let the breath go."

He paused to let me breathe.

"Now focus on that first at-bat. Take your time, but when you feel you're tuned in to it, give me a zero to 10 on the tension in your chest."

"Less again, I'd say about a one, maybe two. It feels pretty good actually. But how..."

"Start tapping," the man cut me off. "Start tapping on your eyebrow and just keep doing laps at a relaxed pace – but this time focus on the DL game."

"That sounds better."

How to Make Yourself Safe

Sensing we were running out of time before my possible final at-bat, the man kept his coaching in fast forward.

"Tap and breathe and go back to that DL game and see what you saw, hear what you heard, and let those feelings come back."

It took me just a few moments to change channels and have the DL game back on. I reconnected with my ABCs and could feel myself **Act Big**, **Breathe Big**, and **Commit Big**. I felt my swagger stepping into the box, the relaxed confidence in my rocking stance, and the effortless fluid swing that launched a Ruthian blast.

"Good," the man said. "Tap and breathe and experience yourself as totally and unstoppably confident."

Several seconds went by and my good feelings grew. I'd made it through more than three full tap laps when the man moved to the next step.

"Now tap on your eyebrow and repeat out loud after me: Even though I have this tension in my chest…"

"Even though I have this tension in my chest," I parroted.

"Tap on the side of your eye and say, I choose to be calm and confident like I was in the DL game."

"I choose to be calm and confident like I was in the DL game."

"Below your eye: Even though I feel this constriction in my energy..."

"Even though I feel this constriction in my energy..."

"I accept myself just the way I am."

That one caught me off guard, but I repeated it anyway.

"Now, under your nose: Even though I struck out badly yesterday..." the man continued.

"Even though I struck out badly in the first inning..."

"Collar bone: And I have hit like a total idiot for the past two weeks..."

"And I have hit like a total idiot for the past two weeks..."

"I choose to be calm and confident like I was in the DL game."

We continued this way through a full tap lap, alternating between the negative focus and the positive, and then a second complete lap. Each time it was "Even though I had this negative thing" on one spot, and "I choose this positive thing" on the next spot.

"Now stop and take a deep breath in through your nose and hold it in your belly... and exhale letting the breath go."

As I did, I noticed I was very relaxed. But energized at the same time. I felt ready to hit. I was calm and enjoying the calm, but eager to get to the plate.

"That's pretty cool," I said. "I feel much better than I did a couple of minutes ago. What..."

"Say this out loud," the man interrupted, obviously on a mission. "I'm an awesome hitter and I'm going to have a great at-bat."

I repeated it and immediately said "10."

"And zero to 10 on that tension in your chest?"

"Gone. Zero."

"Great."

"I love it, but how does it work? You're right that it's a relaxation thing, but I'm not just relaxed, I'm confident."

"I'm not going to bog you down with a lot of explanation. Let's not cloud your head. But tapping is really a form of acupuncture."

"Really? I never believed in that whacky Eastern stuff."

"That's why I wanted to just have you do it first so you wouldn't be thinking about anything but what I asked you to focus on. And as I said, it doesn't matter if you believe in it or not."

"Okay, but how does it work?"

"You already know you're made of energy and energy is flowing through and around you all the time."

"Yes."

"Energy flows through you, especially along energy super highways called meridians. You've got several different ones throughout your body. Fortunately, you don't have to know anything about them other than that you can change the way the energy flows through them by tapping on these particular points where your energy is particularly close to the surface."

"Huh," I half grunted, knowing I was only partially understanding what he was saying.

"So the tapping affects the energy flow in your body."

"That much I can understand. It's weird, but I felt it."

"Tapping speaks the same language your body does: energy. It communicates with your body at a deeper level than words do. That's why I could have said, 'Hey, 21, just relax and be eager to hit' and it wouldn't have helped you much, if at all."

"No, I agree."

"Tapping 'talks' directly to your body, to your subconscious. You could say when you're tapping you're sending a mes-

sage to your Inner Umpire that says 'Everything is okay, I'm actually safe,' at the same time you're tuning in to a memory where your Inner Umpire ruled you not safe."

"So that's how you re-train your Inner Umpire like you mentioned before?"

"Exactly. The tapping gets the Inner Umpire to change his call. So now something that was terrible becomes a non-issue."

"Well, that strike out wasn't good."

"Tapping doesn't change the past," the man said. "It doesn't change what happened. It simply unplugs the emotion from it. It removes the emotional charge the event had for you."

"I see," I said in my 'go on' tone.

"A negative event kicks up a negative emotion. That negative emotion, like frustration, is like an accident on your internal energy highway."

"On a meridian."

"Yes. So just like if you're driving down a highway, say you're driving to Minneapolis on 94 and you come upon an accident. The sirens are going, the lights are flashing, and traffic is quickly backing up."

"Been there."

"Now a trip that should have taken you four hours is going to take a lot longer. It's the same with your internal highways: You send a signal from your brain to throw the ball,

or hit, and it starts out fine but then runs into traffic. The flow of energy is blocked or slowed and your performance suffers."

"I get tense or I get distracted."

"Usually both. When you're in The Bigs, (say a 9,9 on our chart or better) you're free of energy blocks, your energy flows freely. You have full access to your talent and skill. The negative emotions you feel when you're out of alignment with The Bigs are energy blocks. They are 'interference' that will hinder your performance, not to mention your enjoyment of the game."

"So when my Inner Umpire says I'm safe I don't have these energy blocks creating resistance in my body."

"Exactly. In an extreme case, like when a player gets the yips and can't make a simple throw, there's a major pile up along one of the energy highways. Talking about it doesn't help, you need to go in with an emotional tow truck and clear out the negative energy. The tapping goes in and clears the wreck and gets things flowing again."

"But then why does it work to tap and think about playing great?" I asked. "Wouldn't it erase the good feelings too."

"That's a funny one, but no, it enhances the good stuff and releases the bad."

"That's awesome. It keeps it simple."

"That's one of the main reasons I use it."

"But how do you explain that it helps whether you focus on the bad or the good?

"The Field is slanted to the good. Tapping releases emotions that are holding on. So when you're focused on a negative event or emotion, the release makes you fall to the good. And when you're focused on a positive state it releases that and it falls to the good too. So it gets even better."

"I see."

"That's a functional explanation. I can't say I understand everything myself. But I do understand results. And of all the things I've shared with you, tapping is the most powerful."

"Because it talks right to my Inner Umpire?"

"Yes, it talks directly to your subconscious and your subconscious, where all your core beliefs lie, is the dominant force in how your life goes. Yes, you can make moment to moment choices that override your core beliefs, but in the long run, and usually in the short run, your subconscious wins the day."

Finanger had a long at-bat against Kamin, but Kamin eventually got the strike out. Then, Swanson grounded out on three pitches. With Waddle coming up, the chances of me hitting again were getting slim. That is, unless we were able to get a two-out rally going here now or one in the seventh.

I continued with the man: "Couldn't I just focus on the good, like tap and do my ABCs, and skip the bad stuff?"

"It would be better than nothing. But look at it this way: If your dog took a poop on a plate, would putting ice cream on top make it a good dessert?"

"No!" I laughed.

"Well, that's what positive thinking on top of negative thinking is like."

"That's gross."

"Yes. If you're full of blocks of negative energy – that is, if you've got frustration and anger and other low vibration energy inside you, they are like the dog poop. Crappy vibrations."

"They interfere with my game."

"Yes. So you need to tap it out. You need to tap your crap."

I let out a good laugh. "That would be a good book title."

"You could be right," he smiled, "tap your crap. That's really what you do: focus on the negative thoughts, feelings and images in your head and tap."

We both enjoyed the moment and watched Kamin deliver a curveball to Waddle.

"So there are two ways to use the tapping," the man said. "Both are done the same way, using the same basic tap lap process I taught you. The first and most powerful is to go through your past and clear out the negative experiences

stuck in your system. Everybody has some unprocessed negative events clogging their emotional pipes."

"I sure do."

"So you go back and clear out these negative emotions and experiences and in so doing you uncover and change your limiting core beliefs."

"Core beliefs run the show," I said, echoing one of the man's biggest teachings.

"Yes, so this is the heavy duty 'train your Inner Umpire' work. You go through a process, not that it ever fully ends I might add, but you go through and upgrade your belief system so that you are safe and free to play baseball. You bring your Inner Umpire up to the modern age where it isn't life threatening to strike out or fail in any way."

"I doubt we have time for that now."

"No, but you're feeling good. Start tapping now. The more you tap, the better. The second way of using the tapping is how we're using it here. Tapping during a game or just before it."

"I'm kind of out of sight out here," I said, "and desperate, so I've been willing to tap. But do you expect me to be at the plate or in the field tapping?"

"No, no, no. You could, and one day in the future that will be normal. But not now. There are some cool stealth ways to tap so no one knows you're doing it. So the two uses of tapping are to upgrade your Inner Umpire so you feel safe

and free to play great, and during or just before a game to deal with the emotions you have at the moment."

"I want to know how to tap during a game – like before this next at-bat."

"Not enough time for that now, but just tap on that collar bone point for a while. Or just press on that spot and hold it. That's enough to stimulate the pressure point you need. But right now it looks like it's time for you to go."

Waddle had just grounded out again and it was time for the top of the last inning. I hustled in to the dugout, grabbed my glove and ball, and started warming up my infielders.

I could feel my nerves lighting up. I could feel my chest contract, my breathing shallow. This was it. The last inning.

"Act Big, Breathe Big, Commit Big," I said to myself, and then followed my own advice.

Each pitch that inning I thought, *Hit it to me,* and imagined hot ground balls coming my way. None did, but I would have eaten them alive.

Despite the Rakeops' obnoxious fans yelling and hollering, and their dugout chattering without stopping to breathe, we got them out with no change to the score.

We headed to the bottom of the last inning, down one run.

Questions to Consider for Part 8

1. When is positive thinking the WRONG thing to do?

2. Why is it helpful to focus on negative thoughts and feelings while tapping?

3. List the tapping points.

4. Tapping's big strength is it's ability to speak directly to your "Inner Umpire" and change your core_____?

Try tapping yourself now FREE!
To make sure you do it right, tap along with me on a FREE VIDEO at
www.PlayBigTraining.com

Part 9:

"The Ultimate Coaching Message"

You're about to discover...

- How Hank Aaron's hitting approach will improve your entire life

- That top players and coaches know "feeling good" and focusing are the top priorities

- The buried element that determines your success more than anything else

- How the story ends!

The Ultimate Coaching Message

Our last half inning of the season was starting and it was time to be in the dugout to cheer and get ready to hit. As much as I benefited from talking with the man, I needed to be with my teammates.

On my way in from first base, I jogged over to the fence one final time.

"Thanks, mister!"

"You're welcome," he said, "Enjoy yourself."

It felt like good-bye. I was excited to hit, but felt this too brief encounter with this mysterious man, this baseball version of The Lone Ranger, was over. I sensed I wouldn't see him again.

"Talk to you after the game?" I said.

"Gotta go," he said. "You know what you need to do. Keep it simple and practice. Remember: when the student is ready..."

"... the teacher appears," I finished. "I hope it's you next time, too."

"Thank you," he said. I nodded and turned toward the dugout.

"Hey 21," he said, "one more thing."

"Yeah?"

"Start tapping on your collar bone while I say this. It will help it sink in."

I started tap, tap, tapping, happy to get one last booster shot of the man's energy.

"Talk to Stan Musial, Hank Aaron, Billy Williams, Rod Carew, almost any great hitter and they'll tell you their focus was 'put the fat part of the bat on the ball.' In other words, their mission at the plate was simply to connect the fat part of the bat with the ball.

"Let's look at that; the fat part of the bat is the sweet spot, the best part of the bat. The ball is the most important thing to focus on. If you aren't 'all in' with your focus on the ball you won't hit.

"The game is the same for you in all aspects of your life: ***take the best part of you, your sweet spot, The Bigs, and focus it on the most important thing.*** That may be the ball if you're hitting, but also a single question on a test in school, the person you're in a conversation with, the task you're doing at work. Whatever you're doing, identify the 'ball,' the most important thing right now to focus on, and go 'all-in' on it. If you want to be a success at anything, find a way to bring the best of you and connect it with the most important thing."

I lightly pounded my fist into the sweet spot of my mitt as I listened. The sweet spot of anything feels good.

"Sounds like 'feel good and focus,'" I said.

"You got it. But in life, just like in baseball, you can't control your results. Just like you can line out, or a pitcher can make his best pitch and get rocked with a two-run double, you can bring the best of you and connect it with the most important thing and still not get the result you want. ***But I can promise you: If you simply keep coming with that approach, if you relentlessly approach your life the way great hitters approach hitting, you'll really enjoy the ride. And enjoyment, you'll recall, is your purpose.***"

"Got it," I said. I felt tingly energy wave through my body. I felt light, free. A switch had been thrown in my chest, flooding my insides with a wonderful light. A breath dropped all the way down into my belly. I was excited to hit, but the energy wasn't fear, it wasn't anxiousness. It was excitement. I was eager to hit. Maybe I would get a hit to win the game, maybe I wouldn't even get that chance. But I knew I was okay. I was safe either way.

One Last Chance

As the inning began it didn't look like I was going to get a chance to hit. Down a run, our first batter of the inning, Gary Thielen, struck out. I went to the bat rack to start my routine, but I needed three of the next four guys to get on to get a chance to hit.

Joe Knight got our side pumped up with a single on the ground to left. But then Jim George popped out on the first pitch. Our vibe took a serious hit when the ball disappeared in their shortstop's mitt for the second out.

Shockingly, Kamin, who'd been cruising, nailed Lee Swenson on the knee with his first pitch. Swense jogged it off as he headed to first base.

That brought up Kevin Dotseth. Like a bunch of swimmers on the starting blocks waiting for the starting gun to go off, players from both teams were on the top lip of their dugouts waiting to dive onto the field to celebrate.

The first pitch to Dots was a high fastball. Even in the seventh inning, Kamin still had his gas. Dots swung but couldn't catch up with it. Strike one.

The tension was as thick as I'd felt in any game, summer league or not.

With the count 1-1, Kamin rocked and fired, and Dots swung...

ping.

Dots had chased an outside curve ball and rolled a ground ball to the right side of the infield. A routine, easy play by the second baseman and the Rakeops would be doing the dog piling celebration.

Each meager bounce the ball took was like a hammer pounding the nails of our coffin.

Bounce, bounce, bounce...

But wait! The second baseman! The guy with the horrible energy. Had he turned it around?

Bounce, bounce...

Was his energy still blocked? Was his energy still a negative dark red?

Bounce, bounce...

Was he still focused on himself? Was he still contracted like a turtle under attack?

Bounce, bounce...

Was he attracting a....

DOINK!

YES!

The final hop jumped like a firecracker off the dirt. The ball kicked up and hit the bottom edge of the second baseman's protective cup and rolled behind him – but not far.

Dots, our slowest runner, rumbled down the line.

The second baseman swooped up the ball, turned, and fired to first. The throw was hard but low. The first baseman scooped it cleanly – just as Dots' foot thudded into the bag.

The umpire's arms flew violently out to his sides...

SAFE!!!

Both benches went wild, ours with excitement, the Rakeops' with rage.

"He was out!" yelled their bench.

"Great hustle, Dots!" shouted ours. "Way to drive the ball!" they said sarcastically, laughing.

That's all we needed. Two runners on.

Here we go! It all comes down to me...

Every cell of my body glowing with excitement, I took my first step toward home plate.

Then I saw the Rakeops' manager running out to first base to argue the call. He was hot. It was a very close play, probably a tie. The call could have gone either way – but it went ours. Soon their skipper was in the first base umpire's face, letting him have it.

Safe, I smiled to myself. That was the call of the day. Safe. *When you're safe you get to play on, when you're not safe you go home.*

I'm safe. I'm okay no matter what happens here. I'm safe whether I come through here or not.

I can't say I totally felt that was true, probably a seven on the man's zero to 10 scale. At least I knew enough about how I was designed and how things worked to be even able to think straight.

I'm sure their second baseman wasn't feeling too safe.

Tough luck, man, too bad you didn't attract my man to coach you today!

I wondered if he had really attracted a bad hop. *Could that happen? Bad vibes attract bad news, so I guess it's possible.*

Wow.

While the Rakeops' manager spewed low vibrations all over the first base ump, I used the extra time to re-set myself and review what I had learned.

I took a big breath.

What a day. Two days, really. Started so terribly. I felt hopeless, powerless. Very bottom of the vibrational scale.

Then I meet a man – well, I wouldn't know him if I saw him and I don't even know his name, so did I really meet him? And that man coaches me for two games through a fence! He spins together mental exercises, world history lessons,

and some crazy glasses that enable me to see that everything is energy. Then he closes by having me tap on different spots on my body.

But mostly I got that he really cared about me and that he wanted me to get this stuff. I felt honored he saw himself in me and cared enough to offer what he'd learned so I could enjoy a different fate. He wanted me to enjoy myself and to expand myself. That's why I play, so I can't think of a greater gift anyone could give me.

He'd given me the tools to fulfill my purpose. Can't beat that.

I'd learned the Law of Attraction, that like attracts like and that the experiences that come into my life are a vibrational match for what I'm broadcasting into The Field.

I'd learned that because the Law of Attraction governs baseball the way the Law of Gravity governs matter, feeling good is my top priority. Even though that seems

funny, it makes perfect logical sense. When I feel great, when I'm in The Bigs, I play great, and not only is playing great fun, but it's the way to make my bigger goals come true.

Why do I want to achieve big goals in baseball? Because of how reaching them would make me feel.

I wanted to win this championship. Why? Because of how it would make me feel.

Feelings rule. It all made sense to make feeling good my top priority.

I'd learned tools I can use – and need to practice – that help me feel good. I loved the ABCs. Act Big, Breathe Big, Commit Big. I can use that everywhere.

And this tapping thing was pretty strange, but dang if I didn't feel freer and more confident fast. I was excited to learn more about it since the real performance upgrades are in changing my core beliefs. My core beliefs determine my success and enjoyment more than anything else so getting more coaching on that was huge.

But that was for the future. Right now their manager, who should have been kicked out of the game, was walking back to the dugout. His slow gait gave me a few final moments to focus and prepare.

The side show was now over. Time to play the vibrational matching game.

I Reach for My New Goal

Both benches and the crowd were all on their feet yelling. Our dugout had their hats on funny.

Every cell in my body was on its feet screaming (it felt like my cells were doing the wave!).

Tying run on second and the winning run on first. Another double wins the game.

As I made my way to home plate, I took command of my focus. I grabbed my brain's reins.

I could feel my heart pounding and my energy contracting, so I took a slow breath and lifted my head and shoulders.

An image flashed through my mind of my last strike out the day before and how horrible it would be to repeat that now. So I took a quick trip back to DL and saw myself effortlessly crushing that home run off the light tower.

Then the voice in my head started.

"Don't choke," it said. *"Don't be the goat that loses it."*

"Thank you for sharing," I thought, "I'm going to see the ball and put the fat part of the bat on it."

"I could be the hero!"

"Just do your ABCs."

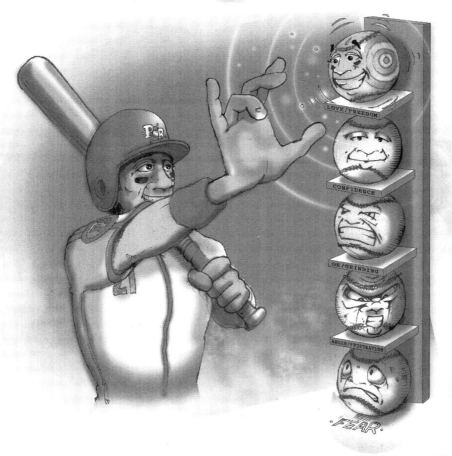

"A home run here would be awesome! Imagine how they'd mob me!"

"Just do your ABCs."

But I really want to get a hit.

"See the ball; put the fat part of the bat on it."

I walked deliberately behind the umpire and approached the batter's box as if it was mine.

Green Light Routine. I cleared the batter's box with my right foot. Checked third base for signs.

Act Big: I shuttered my shoulders and pressed up through the crown of my head. *I'm the king and this is my domain.*

Breathe Big: I firmly planted my back foot in the box. I inhaled big (although only into my chest – I was too energized to get it all the way down to my belly), and exhaled as I put my front foot down.

Commit Big: I rocked forward and back, forward and back, picking my heels up each time as I repeated *"See the ball and put the fat part on it. See the ball and put the fat part on it..."*

I could sense Kamin's powerful energy pouring down on home plate. This guy was an animal and he wasn't going to go down easy.

"See the ball and put the fat part on it."

Kamin rocked back and fired...

I rocked back to release a swing...

Man, I love this feeling!

Looking back on that moment now I can tell you I'd won the game before Kamin even let go of the last pitch.

In that moment I decided the real game was being played on The Field of energy.

I'd won because I'd focused my energy in such a way that I was a vibrational match for what I wanted. That's all a guy can do in any given moment.

Does feeling good and focusing guarantee I'll get the results I want every time? No.

But success isn't a destination to get to or some goal to achieve, it's a feeling. I can win no matter what happens on the field.

In that moment I got clear what I wanted to do with the rest of my life. I wanted to Play Big.

THE END

Find out at:

PlayBigBaseball.com

Are YOU Ready to
PLAY BIG?

Come now to

www.PlayBigTraining.com

and get all this training **FREE!** *($150 VALUE)*

1. **The "ABC" Exercise**

2. **A workbook to deepen your learning**

3. **"Feel Good and Focus Chart" downloads**

4. **Unpublished book excerpts**

5. **Tapping Video to Remove Stress and Fear**

All the knowledge in this book will go to waste if you don't take action. All great players have coaches. Get yours now FREE at

www.PlayBigTraining.com

Try tapping yourself now **FREE!**

To make sure you do it right, tap along with me on a FREE VIDEO at

www.PlayBigTraining.com

©2011 Dr. Tom Hanson

TROUBLE THROWING?

Dr. Tom Hanson is a world leader in eliminating the "baseball yips" – the throwing problem that devastated the careers of **Chuck Knoblauch**, **Rick Ankiel** (as a pitcher), **Steve Sax** and thousands of others who never made it to the Major Leagues.

Don't let your playing days
be cut short by this curable condition.

With Dr. Tom's advanced technology
you can beat the yips.

For more information and to read success stories, visit

www.YipsBeGone.com

"Dr. Tom's done wonders for my throwing!"

Jarrod Saltalamacchia, *Catcher, Boston Red Sox*

©2011 Dr. Tom Hanson

Got an Organization You'd Like to PLAY BIG?

Bring **Dr. Tom Hanson** in to speak!

His dynamic, interactive style brings home the life-changing principles in this book.

For business groups Hanson blends his extensive experience coaching top executive and sales people to breakthrough results with engaging stories from baseball greats to create a memorable, performance enhancing experience.

For more information, write his office at
info@PlayBigTraining.com or call **813-968-8863**

Also check out the business coaching site:

www.HeadsUpPerformance.com

IF YOU DON'T PLAY OR COACH BASEBALL...

PLAY BIG is much more than a baseball book. The powerful ideas in PLAY BIG can also help you...

- **Double your effectiveness at work**
- **Increase your income exponentially**
- **Finally lose the weight and get into good physical shape**
- **Create the relationships of your dreams**
- **Be more happy and fulfilled!**

Go now to *www.PlayBigTraining.com* to get "life" versions of

- **The ABC exercise**
- **"Feel Good and Focus Chart" download**
- **Tapping Video to Remove Stress and Fear (tap along with me and see what the excitement is all about)**
- **And much more.... FREE!**

All the knowledge in this book will go to waste
if you don't take action. All great performers have coaches.

Get yours now FREE at
www.PlayBigTraining.com

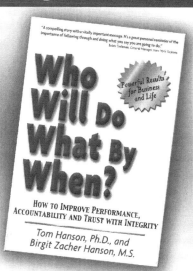

The Illustrator/Designer

Todd Pearl is an accomplished freelance illustrator
and award-winning designer. From illustrating children's
books to designing high-end corporate brand development,
Todd is your one-stop creative shop!

Todd resides in Clawson, MI, just outside of Detroit with
his wife Lisa and their two dachshunds, Stella and Cooper.

View Todd's work at ***www.toddpearl.com***